The MLM Magic Workbook

Companion workbook to the
award-winning book
*MLM Magic: How An
Ordinary Person Can Build An
Extra-Ordinary Networking Business
From Scratch.*

Venus Catherine Andrecht

Margaret L. McWhorter
Ransom Hill Press
PO Box 325
Ramona, CA 92065

Printing History:
First edition - August 1994

Credits:
Author - Venus Catherine Andrecht
Editor - Summer Andrecht

ISBN 0-941903-11-7

Note

This book was written as a companion to the book *MLM Magic: How An Ordinary Person Can Build An Extra-Ordinary Networking Business from Scratch*. You will notice that page numbers are listed under headings throughout this Workbook that correspond to similar topics in *MLM Magic*. This Workbook is intended to be written in as you explore the exercises.

Author's Note

A few weeks ago my mother, Margaret, said, "Venus, you need to write a workbook to go with your book, *MLM Magic*."

I looked at my mother and said, "You have frogs in your head. No."

Mom said, "But you need it for the classes you teach, and everybody keeps asking me if you have more books, or tapes. . .just anything! They need more help."

"Mom," I answered, "I'm doing a column, working on two more tapes and booklets, writing another book, plus running several businesses, and you want me to do a workbook, too?!"

"By next Tuesday," Mom said. "You could use it at your next class."

"By next Tuesday?!" I was incredulous. "You want me to write this book by *next Tuesday*?"

Mom and I had been having tea. I put my cup down with a thunk and said, "I'm going home."

As I stood up to go, I assured my mother that putting a workbook together was a stupid idea. It was too involved—and it certainly couldn't be done by Tuesday!

Later that evening, as I sat in my red-checked chair with my black and white cat on my lap, I thought, "You know, Mom's got a darn good idea. *MLM Magic* does need a workbook."

I started remembering all the things I'd done when I first started working my successful multilevel business. As I sat there scratching the cat, everything came back to me in a great rush of pictures, details, and emotion. I recalled exactly what actions had led to my success and, of course, I realized that I'd be happy and grateful and glad to be able to share further information with you, my friends out in Multilevel Land!

So, I snatched up an old battered notebook and began writing frantically. I knew that if mother was with me now, as I was fanning my flaming pinwheel of creativity, she'd be shouting, "Use the computer! Use the computer!" But, I didn't have time for that.

Three hours later, this book was largely written. I was exhausted and wound so tight I couldn't sleep most of the night.

The next day, I took my grubby little notebook over to Mom.

"I wrote the Workbook," I said.

Mom looked at me, hang-jawed.

"You did?" she said.

"Yes." I handed her the notebook. She said what I expected. Actually, she yelled.

"It's all handwritten! Why didn't you use the computer! It'd be so easy if you had it on the computer!"

"I know," I apologized. "But the computer's too slow for me. I'm always losing the little arrow, and I think I have to correct everything and be professional and I just wanted to get this all down. And now," I added slyly, "it's your turn. You can figure out what I said and put it in order. You always make me look like I know what I'm doing."

Mom looked both delighted and horrified at the mess I'd brought her.

"Well," I said as I left, "let's see what *you* can do by Tuesday."

The Workbook that follows was not finished by the Tuesday in question, but here it is. As Mom was editing it over weeks and months, she kept saying, "I can't believe you did this in three hours!"

That's something that sometimes happens with writers. A mental door gets sprung open and all the room's contents drop out on the floor.

When my mother brought this Workbook back to me for its first correction, I scanned over it slowly.

Every once in a while, I would pause and say, "Did I write this? I don't remember writing this."

"Ah well," Mom admitted, "I think maybe I did."

Mom knows me and how I work so well, that somehow, in the end, sometimes neither one of us remembers who "fixed" what.

Last week a man called and complimented me on the first book I wrote, *The Outrageous Herb Lady*. He said, "You know, I learned more about multilevel in the last four pages of that book than I learned in all the MLM books I'd read previously."

"You did?" I said, completely astonished. I certainly couldn't remember revealing MLM's secrets in the last four pages of a book about having an herbal health business that I'd written years before.

"Yep," the man said, "I did. You made it all so simple. Why couldn't the other writers have just summed it all up like you did?" I didn't know.

I didn't know until, feeling suspicious, I looked at the last four pages of the revised edition of *The Outrageous Herb Lady*. Yep. The four pages were written by my mother!

So, I present you this Workbook. It's filled with my ideas, my writing, my "secrets," my "successes," and my life. . .as far as I can recall! But, you'll find my mother's fingers everywhere, and I think it's time we give her credit!

Table of Contents

1

An Entrepreneurial Assessment

(See pp. 30-38 in *MLM Magic*.)

To begin with, this questionnaire will help you assess your qualities to see how suited you are to being an entrepreneur. Not everyone is happy working for him or herself. The time to discover this is now, before you spend a lot of time, energy, and money in a business that you won't enjoy or succeed in.

Review Your Abilities

A. Natural Abilities: What have you always found easy to do? Can you sing under water? Catch gophers? Sell Christmas Cards? Talk people into anything? Find the good in any event? Sleep anywhere, anytime? Fix holes in socks? Look good when you get up in the morning? Play musical instruments with your cats?

As an example, a person's list might look like this:

1. I speak well to a crowd.
2. Women like me.
3. I'm good at helping others.
4. When I plant cosmos flowers they often grow taller than my house.
5. I'm the best driver in my family. I could have been a race car driver.

Now list *your* natural abilities. List everything you can think of. It's amazing, but everything you've ever done or learned will be useful.

My Natural Abilities:

_____

_____

_____

_____

_____

_____

_____

_____

_____

_____

_____

_____

B. Creativity: Some of your natural abilities can also fit in here. Can you paint, draw, write, speak well, or build things? Write down where you feel your creativity comes through in your life. Also ask yourself, "What did I do well as a kid?"

Examples:

1. I create and sew my own patterns.
2. I'm the best cook I know of.
3. I can paint parrots while I hang upside down.
4. I have the most intriguing daydreams.
5. I can build amazing things out of blocks and tinker toys.
6. I'm good with color and design.

Now make your list.

How I'm Creative:

_____

_____

_____

_____

_____

_____

_____

_____

_____

_____

_____

_____

C. Entrepreneurship: Are you ahead of your time? Can you think of things that few others think of? Things that work? Do you read books before they become best-sellers? Do you do things before they become popular? Are you able and willing to do something different? Do you do well without a nine to five job? What did you do as a kid to earn money or get what you wanted?

   Examples:

   1. I grew my own radishes as a kid and sold them on the street corner.
   2. I sold butter and cream to my neighbors when we were short on money.
   3. I offered to cut grass and feed my neighbors' animals when they were on vacation.
   4. I named my kid Jennifer two years before the entire United States did the same.

Give some examples of your own entrepreneurship:

How Have I Been Entrepreneurial?

_____

_____

_____

_____

_____

_____

_____

_____

_____

_____

_____

_____

D. Persistence: Write out instances where you persisted. How long did you persist and what was the outcome?

Examples:

1. I persuaded my spouse to get a hearing aid when he/she thought it wasn't needed. It took over a year.

2. I learned to play the piano even though my family begged me to stop practicing.

3. I stayed married twenty years longer than anyone thought I could.

4. I went to night school for two years and got my diploma.

Your turn: Where have you persisted?

Where Have I Persisted?

_____

_____

_____

_____

_____

_____

_____

_____

_____

_____

_____

_____

E. Resourcefulness: How and where have you triumphed, perhaps when no one else thought you would? Maybe it's as simple as figuring out how to change a light bulb in a 10-foot high yard light that doesn't have screws. Think all the way back to your childhood.

Examples:

1. I figured out how to put a bicycle together in spite of the poor directions.

2. I persuaded my kids to settle for a toy wagon when they really wanted a real car.

3. I used materials I had on hand to create a smashing, expensive-looking cocktail dress.

4. I can make a dinner out of nothing.

5. I managed in a foreign country all by myself where I knew no one.

Let's see what you've done. How have you been resourceful? Make your own list now.

How Have I Been Resourceful?

_____

_____

_____

_____

_____

_____

_____

_____

_____

_____

F. What Others Say: What Mom, Auntie, siblings, and old friends say you were like as a kid is important. Get it all down. Keep this page marked in your Workbook for a few days. Write down other memories and ideas as they come to you and as your family remembers them. The idea is for you to become aware of your talents, your habits, and your uniqueness through other peoples' memories of you. But, be prepared to find out things you don't want to know. For example, I had an unsettling revelation about my character the other day. I threw a tea party for female family and friends. Among others, I invited two women who'd been my mother's best friends when I was a kid. Midway through the party, I sat down across from them as they were chatting with three of my sisters and a cousin.

Alice and Shirley were busily recounting stories from when they knew us all best. I was about eight years old at that time. Always thinking that I need more useful information about my innate character, I prodded the two ladies to tell us about our personality traits at that age. I had a big sappy grin and I exuded charming charisma as I waited for my impressive character printout.

"Well," Alice began as she leaned toward me across the table, "your brother Jim was always very close to the surface!" She and Shirley jabbed each other and roared as we all laughed. Jim is incredibly likable, but his emotions are like loose, lit fireworks.

"And sister Polly here," she said, pausing to pass a croupy, rattling smokers cough, "well, we didn't know Polly that well because she was in the hospital that year."

Polly, sitting next to me, looked extremely disappointed.

"Don't worry," I whispered to her, "I remember exactly how rotten you were."

"And me? And me?" I said excitedly.

Alice and Shirley looked at each other. Fifteen seconds of eternity passed in silence. Then, "You were mean," Alice said. She curled her lip.

"Mean? I was mean?" I couldn't believe it, as sweet as I am now!

"Yes, you were mean," Shirley seconded her. "You were always after the kids. You had those long fingernails."

"And," Alice added helpfully, "you had to control everything."

"That's just great," I said, stunned. "That's just great. I'm so glad to know that about myself. I'm certain that can help me with my character improvement project."

Alice squirmed a little. She took a sip of tea, looked at Shirley, and then back at me.

"Ah yes," she said gaily, obviously hoping to soothe me, "you always had flair, Venus. I'd have to say that about you."

"Yes," Shirley nodded. "You still have it, today."

Alice shifted to her right, toward my youngest sister Candy, and touched her cheek. "But, you Candy," she cooed, "you were like a little rose petal. So soft. So sweet. I adored you."

Candy smiled at me like a lizard, I thought. The women went on to other topics. I sat and scratched my arm and felt sorry for myself. I watched the tea party buzzing around me as the ladies ate the crumpets and sand-

7

wiches and cakes and tea provided by Venus the Mean and Controlling.

Alice looked over at me and squinted her eyes.

"And that's another thing," she noted. "You were always very observant. You watched everything. . .but now Candy," she repeated, "Candy was a rose petal."

My friends, I've told you about this tea party and my foray into the past to alert you. You may not like what people tell you about yourself, but you've got me for company and sympathy. Just remember, you need to know these things, because every bit of your natural character can be used for your success in multilevel.

After a lot of thought about Alice and Shirley's insights, I feel that the meanness they noted has been pretty much kicked out of me through the years, and now maybe I'm a bit too nice. A pleasant personality helps in this business. As for my need to control, I've used that trait to gain control of my life. No more nine to five. I'm living my life now exactly as I want to live it. As for natural flair and observation, these traits have helped me a lot with my writing, and certainly with building a multilevel business. Many times I've been in uncomfortable situations with crowds or strangers. Like many of us, I've started feeling uneasy, less able, shy, not as good as, or whatever. When that happens, I pause, and instead of feeling sorry for myself or left out, I start watching. I watch people and I listen. Then, I put what I've noticed to good use.

Here are a few examples of what might come up about your character as family and friends remember you from babyhood on:

1. Mom always tells about the time I stood up to my big brother when I knew I was right and he was wrong.

2. Aunt Ellie often reminds me of the time I convinced her to buy a box of my homemade Christmas cards when she thought she really wanted some store-bought ones.

3. My sister remembers the time I talked her into entering a beauty contest. She says she knew she couldn't win, but I convinced her she could, and she did.

4. Mom says I was always introspective.

5. My brother reminded me of how I dreamed up a game to play at school that was so good the teachers incorporated it into PE.

What Other People Say About My Character:

_____

_____

_____

_____

_____

_____

_____

_____

_____

_____

_____

G. Do you like people? This is the most important question of all: If you don't like people, having all the other qualities combined won't make up for this most important quality. If you do like people, the other qualities are helpful, but not essential.

Also, remember that since you intend to work with people, you have to be sure that your person is not offensive to others.

Checklist For Personal Obnoxiousness

(See p. 87 in *MLM Magic*.)

• **Do you swear?** Sometimes we say things that offend other people without our realizing it. Listen to yourself or ask an honest friend to let you know how your language checks out. As an example, I had a friend in college named Judy. She was a short, fat, Italian girl with black hair and sensuous lips. Judy was very excitable, explosive, and outspoken. She was also prone to shouting "S - - -!" whenever circumstances called for it.

She was cured of her habit one day, however. We were standing in yet another long line at school as we waited to sign up for one more something. There was one delay and foul up after another. The line of students was quiet, sunk into apathy and resignation. All except for Judy. True to her volatile nature, she kept pacing and popping and exploding and yelling a frustrated "S - - -!" every few minutes. Nobody in the line said a word to each other or responded to Judy's temper and mouth. After twenty minutes, the stagnant air seemed to be literally hung with excrement. The silence was pierced only by one more "S - - -!" and then another. It was a gruesome experience, and, as it turned out, one that even Judy felt.

Later that evening she slunk into my dorm room.

"Did I," she whispered, her black eyes round as dimes, "sound as bad as I think I did, today?"

"Yes," I said, "you did."

Judy looked horrified as she slapped her fingers to her lips. "Gawd," she breathed. "It was awful. I never knew how bad I sounded when I swore!"

That was the last time Judy ever said the big "S" word. I don't know if it has anything to do with it, but, shortly after she stopped swearing, she met a handsome fellow and got married.

• **Next, ask yourself, "How's my breath?"** Again, when I was in college, there was a perfectly darling man who had a big crush on me. His one fault was that he had nauseating breath. It was the kind that permeates and clears a crowded room. Being young, I didn't know how to tell him what the problem was. Instead, I resorted to hiding in the closet when he dropped by the apartment, which forced my unwilling roommate to entertain and smell him. The poor man was a nice guy with much to offer besides his odor, but I could never get past that. If you stink, no one will be open to *your* proposals, either.

• **Are you too sexy or odd looking, or acting or smelling?** Other women don't like to be around too sexy a woman (and women are your prospects too, remember), and some men (also your prospects) like it too much.

Are you scary looking, dirty, or do you have greasy hair? Maybe you just think your look is in style, but regular, common folk might think your mind looks like your hairdo.

Do you wash your clothes often enough? If in doubt, sniff your clothes every day. Brush your teeth twice a day. Do all this even if you think your body is different from the rest of ours. I've had people tell me, "Oh, I don't sweat," or, "My hair is so dry I only need to wash it once in a while." Maybe so, but dry heads and bodies can still smell funny.

• **Do you smoke?** More and more people find smokers offensive. Yesterday I got a packet in the mail from a lady who wants me to join her in her health-oriented multilevel. I opened the envelope up and all the papers and samples dropped out, saturated with old cigarette smoke! It sure didn't smell healthy to me.

• **Is your car clean?** People judge us by the way our car looks. If your car is dirty, people will think that you are, too.

• **Is your house or office clean?** I recently went to a distributor's home office. What a dirty, mad, rotten mess it was. As a regular person, I would never have bought product from her or signed with her.

• **Do people like you?** Do they trust and respect you? If not, work on your character while your upline helps you with prospects and downline.

Hopefully, you came through this test with high marks, and you're ready to get busy.

2

Make A Commitment

(See pp. 43-55 in *MLM Magic*.)

Make a commitment to your business. It's important to do this. If you don't, instead of revving up and making those calls after your long, devil-filled day at The Real Job, it'll be too easy to sag into your old chair at night, burp contentedly, and doze through the evening. If you don't make a commitment to your business, you'll simply fade out from it when it doesn't make you millions in the first year.

Here's the commitment I made when I first started my business:

"I commit to one year of constant work, night and day around my Real Job, before I reevaluate. No matter how depressed, or mad, or discouraged I get, I'm not reevaluating until this one year is up!"

You might add: "I commit to be loyal to my company, unless the company proves itself to be wrong for my needs. I realize that switching from one MLM to another, or working with more than one, without a *very* compelling reason, undermines my successful outcome." (The very compelling reason might be that your old MLM company is not right for you anymore, and you need to phase out of it for various reasons. A noncompelling reason would be, "Gosh! I bet if I worked two or more MLMs at once I'd make a truck load of money!" or, "Shoot. Old George says I can make thousands of dollars a week in his superior multilevel." It doesn't work like that in MLM.)

Write out your commitment to your company now:

<u>**My Commitment:**</u>

_____

_____

_____

_____

_____

_____

_____

_____

_____

_____

_____

_____

Once you've made the decision to work MLM and have chosen a company, it's time to do some magnificent and productive daydreaming.

How To Daydream Your Way To Success

(See pp. 239 and 246 in *MLM Magic*.)

Take time to discover what you really want out of life. Take an honest look at yourself—at your goals, your abilities, and your personality. What do I mean by *honest*?

Here is my mother's list of what's important to her:

1. Take time to exercise to improve my health and energy.
2. Take time to enjoy my family and friends.

3. Clean and organize my house.

4. Organize my business and make some money.

5. Learn my computer thoroughly.

I looked at her list and said, "Mom, you've got that upside down. You spend all your time on your computer and never take time for anything else."

She looked surprised, then said, "You're right." Since then, she's been struggling to get in line with reality.

Here's the kind of list I wrote when I first started my MLM business. It's only a partial list, and it's just one of several:

1. I want to get up in the morning and say, "What do I want to do today?" I want everyday to be open to whatever I want to do.

2. I want to notice the seasons as they come and go. I want to be able to sit outside whenever it suits me.

3. I want to have the time to write more books.

4. I want to spend more time with family and friends.

5. I want time to take little trips, just uptown, or, to another state.

6. I want the time to hunker down with my cat and see the world she sees. (I've actually done this, now. The other day, I got down by the sliding glass door with her in my bedroom, and together we watched a little brown spider and a little black ant as they went about their lives. Then, we looked closely at the door frame for a time and thought about whether we'd go outside and listen for gophers in the grass, or sit in the sunny house for a bit longer. We chose the sun and napped together for half an hour. I like her lifestyle.)

After seven years in my multilevel business, I'm doing all the things on that list, and more. For example, this morning I had a late breakfast on my patio under a tall pine tree. A shiny little mockingbird sat on the very top, like a Christmas ornament, and sang the songs of at least ten different birds. I had never heard a bird do that. Of course, mockingbirds are known for that, but I'd never had the time, before, to think it through.

You may have noticed that in this section I'm not talking much about setting goals. It's very important to know where you're going and to have a plan on how to get there, but I've noticed that some of us don't do well with rigid goals. When I started my business, I tried setting strict goals like popular books and seminars advocate. But saying, "In two months I will have achieved the Diamond Rigor Mortis Status within my company, and in two years I will be making $5,000 a month," can be very disheartening if you don't make it. I prefer to say, "I'm going to *work* for Diamond Rigor Mortis Status and $5,000 a month." This takes the pressure off and I can go at my own pace. Of course, the things I want are *always* in my mind, and I'm *always* working for them, in one way or another.

Real daydreaming, not strict goal setting, is my favorite way to build a business or to get anything I want. I especially like to sit or lie where I can look up and see the clouds as they laze or rush across that big blue upside-down bowl that covers the earth. I can spend minutes, hours, or all day doing this. As I watch, I find myself grinning with joy and a great sense of expansion and happiness.

I remember reading an article written by a man in prison. He said that as long as he could see the sky, he never felt like he was imprisoned. That's how I feel, too, and somehow, when I've watched the sky and felt it for awhile, all kinds of unusual and useful ideas begin to come to me. These ideas are often implemented into my MLM business, or into my writing.

School taught us that daydreaming was bad. Remember your cold, ugly, and perhaps windowless school that prevented you from daydreaming and becoming distracted from the *important stuff* you were being taught? I suspect, however, that most things of real value originated from people's daydreams, and not from textbooks.

Here's something I came up with while daydreaming that I practice now: In my mind, I picture money and prosperity raining on me from all good sources. I see the right people coming into my life to join me in my life and work. I picture and give time to this visualization everyday, many times a day. I also picture and believe wholeheartedly that I'm extraordinarily lucky. And what happens? First, I put myself out in the world so these people can come to me. In other words, I socialize. I also work. Then. . .it happens.

A few days ago, I was in a restaurant lunching with a prospect. I was telling her how I imagine money and golden coins raining on me all the time. Moments later, a waiter walked by, tripped a bit, and showered me with coins from a tray he was carrying! I said, "See what I mean?"

Daydreaming and letting the good come to you doesn't mean you sit around and act like a booby. You picture what you want, put yourself where you can receive it, and are alert and leap into action when it enters.

Here's your assignment: Find a nice, comfortable, happy place and start your daydreaming. Write down everything that you visualize having in your life.

After you've done this, take some time to do nothing but dream.

What I Want In My Life:

_____

_____

_____

_____

_____

_____

_____

_____

_____

_____

_____

_____

Make A Wish List

(See pp. 40 and 189 in *MLM Magic.*)

After you get your major dreams written down, it's time to list the specifics of what you want your business to help you get. Create a wish list for yourself. Write down specific things or situations that you want for yourself and which are not too far out of reach. Here is my example of a wish list:

<u>My Wish List</u>

1. Get a new car.
2. Have enough money to pay the bills, with a lot left over.
3. Get the dog's teeth fixed.
4. Get enough money to move out of my mother's house.

Now make your own list.

What I Want My MLM Business To Do For Me:

_____

_____

_____

_____

_____

_____

_____

_____

_____

_____

_____

_____

Put a copy of this list on your refrigerator or your bathroom mirror. You want it to be someplace where you will see it and review it every day.

You've heard over and over how effective visualization (daydreaming) is, but it always seems so esoteric and unreachable. Whole books are written on the subject, so it must work for somebody. Let me tell you something. It does work, and it's not difficult. In fact, it's simple. You've heard the saying, "What you think is what you get," and Jesus even advised us to ask for what we want and assured us we could have it. So write out your wish list and keep thinking about the items on it. Having that list where you can see it reminds you, when you feel like quitting your business, what you're working for.

What I Need To Earn Monthly This Year
(See pp. 251-253 in *MLM Magic*.)

Periodically, I used to sit down and figure out how much money I needed to cover the bare essentials. Then, I'd add a clump on top of that for the big unexpected things that seem to pop up every month.

It's important to list your expenses so you have a realistic idea of how much money you need to make in multilevel. Once you know that, then you can plan how you're going to get it.

You will need to keep a record for a month or two of everything you spend so that you will have an accurate idea of your expenses. You may discover that you are spending a lot of money on frivolous things. The secret to having money is not just to make it, but to use what you have wisely.

It's important to get on top of your expenses. Desperation may spur you to make a commitment to become successful, but living on the edge can make you frantic. Believe me, people can see those spinning dollar signs in your eyes, and they'll leap in the air and take off when they see them start to twirl.

The secret to success is to always approach people from their point of view. No matter how much you need money, never push someone into doing something that isn't right for him or her. Say "Next," and move on.

Your assignment is to write out a record of what you need monthly. Remember to include taxes, insurance, medical expenses, and car repair costs. Here's an example:

19

My monthly expenses:
1. Rent: $800
2. Utilities: $200
3. Food: $450
4. Cat food: $20
5. Etc.

My Monthly Expenses:

_____

_____

_____

_____

_____

_____

_____

_____

_____

_____

_____

3

Setting Up Your Office

Items You'll Need In Your Business

Check off as acquired:

1. Appointment book. (See p. 59 in *MLM Magic.*) I like having a big doctor's size book that I can fill up. Keep track of all your appointments, people to contact, and things you need to do. Fill it out, daily.

2. An MLM work journal. (See p. 57 in *MLM Magic.*)

The first thing to acquire as you plan your business success is an MLM work journal. Your MLM work journal is where you will record all your dreams, thoughts, ideas, notes from company or training meetings, and anything even remotely connected to your work life. It's a place, also, to keep the inspirations that this Workbook will hopefully trigger off in your head.

Get an attractive notebook or blank-paged book that you can carry with you all the time. Take it with you to meetings and trainings for note-taking. Keep it next to you as you walk around the house, or drive your car. Write down creative ideas for your business, names for your prospect list, ideas from other people, stories for your newsletter, or ideas for classes to teach and articles to write. You never know where you might be when you get ideas for your business. There are some nice books available with blank pages. Mine is bright red, so I won't lose it, and it has a flowered cover. A plain, spiral bound notebook will also do.

3. Three-ring binders. (See p. 184 in *MLM Magic.*) I have a number of three-ring binders. They're all different colors so I can keep them straight. I use a big felt-tip pen to write their subject titles on them.

I keep a binder for each year I'm in business. For example, on the side and front of one, with my black felt-tip pen, I have written "1994." I put an original copy of everything I mail to my downline in that year in this binder, including newsletters and company information. At this point, I'm putting copies of all my royalty checks in there too, although you might want to keep a separate binder for them, like I used to.

I also used to keep a separate binder for my distributors, another binder for managers/supervisors (whatever your company calls the higher levels of distributorship), and still another for prospects. Now, I use folders. Do what's easiest and most simple for you. What I'm trying to tell you is that you need to have some kind of system to keep your business in order.

4. Rolodex, portable phone book, or file box for names, addresses, and phone numbers. (See p. 186 in *MLM Magic*.) Even if you keep your mailing list on a computer, it isn't always convenient to open up your computer or interrupt what you're doing when you want to make a call.

5. Stickers with your name and phone number printed on them. (See p. 186 in *MLM Magic*.) Stick these on envelopes and samples of product. Of course, as I mention in *MLM Magic*, I prefer to write my name and phone number with a felt-tip pen on product samples. It looks less premeditated, like I'm not a "real" salesperson.

6. Felt-tip pen for writing your name and address on everything.

7. Folders, plastic sheets, lined paper, and spiral notebooks. (I explain their uses elsewhere in this Workbook.)

Assignment: Write down anything else you will need for your business.

Items I Need In My Business:

_____

_____

_____

_____

_____

_____

_____

_____

_____

_____

_____

Office Equipment

You will gradually want to acquire the following equipment. Unless you have extra money stashed in your pants, or you're coming into a fat inheritance from Aunt Dudie, wait until your business demands these items.

• **Computer:** A computer will streamline writing your newsletter and managing your mailing list.

• **Fax Machine:** Unless all of your downline have fax machines, or your company uses them to get out major news, it can wait. I have to admit, though, that I'm in love with mine. I still can't fathom how all those pictures and writings can drop right out of the sky and roll out in front of me in seconds. I feel like an aborigine receiving messages from the space gods.

• **Photocopier**: You will get tired of traipsing off to the copy shop. I use my copier every day, many times a day. Get one as soon as it makes sense. Make it a simple one, though. At first, I didn't do that. I bought a refurbished one for $7,000. (There is no justification for having a copier of this size and complexity with your business. I had fallen under the spell of a Super Salesman who smelled a sucker on sight.) For $7,000, used, you can imagine the size of that machine and everything it was supposed to do. However, because it was so enormous and complicated, it almost never worked, and the yearly maintenance fee was outrageous and kept going up. Finally, after I had fought with it for years, in desperation I called the Salvation Army and begged them to come and get it. Two giant men arrived and worked valiantly to get that dragon-sized copier into their truck. They immediately dropped and bounced it in the street. It was the actual size of a small piano and made as much noise when it hit the ground. Then the muscle-men hoisted it up once again and jerked it to the truck, where, quite gracefully, it flipped, rolled out, and smacked the street, again, headfirst. I kind of winced and drew my shoulders up, but I didn't say a thing. It had never worked much anyway, and I've always wondered if it's worked at all, since.

• **Cordless telephone:** This kind of phone makes all your phone calls easier. Having it makes me want to be on the phone more, because I have the freedom to keep moving while talking. With a cordless phone, I can fold clothes, feed the animals, or sit naked by the pool and do business.

• **File cabinet:** Just get something simple, but you need something. Otherwise, your piles of important papers get scattered all over and it'll make you mad.

Get all of the above as soon as you can afford them. These items are not essential, but they make life easier.

Assignment: Write down anything you think you need now or will need in the future. Plan how and when and where you'll get these items.

Example:
1. I need all of the above, plus:
2. A table from the thrift store.
3. The lamp from the extra bedroom.
4. A vase of flowers.

Office Equipment I Need:

_____

_____

_____

_____

_____

_____

_____

_____

_____

_____

_____

_____

A Beautiful Life

You can make your office or work area very simple and inexpensive, but put beauty around you. It's important to feed your soul while you're attempting to feed yourself and your family with this business. Bright flowers, pictures, and music will add a lot to your work life. If you'll look at the back of my book, *MLM Magic,* you'll see a picture of me in my kitchen office in jeans with my bare feet up on a table. You'll notice my decorations: a picture of an angel and another of Christ; a wicker duck that holds letters, papers, and pens and pencils; a flower calendar; art postcards; a book with a gilt-gold cover; and a carved letter opener. I use bright red and patterned ribbons for book marks, I light scented candles, and I usually have a soft cat or two on the table and a happy dog at my feet.

Yes, the table and wall are messy, but they are messy with wonderful things. I like to be where nice smelling, lovely looking and feeling things are, so I'm inclined to spend more time at this table, working, when I have pretty things surrounding me.

This isn't just for women. You men can do this, too. Have things around you that you like to touch, feel, look at, and smell.

And back to those jeans I'm wearing. Since I work a lot at home, I can dress comfortably. In fact, one of my personal rules in life is to only buy and wear clothes that are either completely comfortable, or that make me look like a flaming knock-out. Just notice, however, that when I'm working at home I get dressed in the morning, like everyone else. It's not psychologically good for you to sit around in your old rumpled nightshirt or your dingy nightgown all day. Do wear what feels good, though. Wearing what you want is one of the perks in a business like this.

Looking back at your last assignment, you may want to add some beautiful items to that list.

(For more information on how to set up your business, office, taxes, and how not to overspend on anything, order my audio and booklet, *Money Out Of Control*, published by Ransom Hill Press. 1-800-423-0620)

4

Prospecting

Where Can I Find Prospects For My Business?
(See pp. 65-80 and 115 in *MLM Magic*.)

Now that your business is sort of set up and your mind is clear, surely you realize that to build this business, you need distributors. In order to get them, you need prospects. Finding people and getting them into the business seems to be the biggest, toughest, scariest concern for most distributors. When you're new at this, you're happy and glad to find and sign just anyone. Most people haven't even *thought* about finding and signing only the *right* prospects. So let's put that idea off for a moment. Let's concentrate now on just finding people for you to approach.

In the past, many distributors have looked at me with despair hanging off their faces while they said, "I've talked to everyone I know. There's no one left to talk to!"

Here are some ideas:

1. *Contact people who advertise for mates in newspapers.* Why not? If they don't have love, how about money? Why should they be lonely. . .and poor, too? You can tell them that when they're in a multilevel they'll have lots of excuses for approaching people.

2. *Take a night class at your local high school or college.* Try an ROP (Regional Occupational Program) class. They're free. These are put together by the government to teach people different trades and skills. (Your local library has this information.) The people who go to classes are often looking for ways to increase their incomes or improve their lives. Also, being with the same people week after week builds relationships, and that's what turns prospects into distributors.

3. *Attend dance classes.*

4. *Go to church.*

5. *Go to the dog show next month.* All you have to do there is love dogs and the dog owners will love you. Comment on someone's dog: "Quite a bonny little dog you have there. Quite a handsome fellow." Meanwhile, you should be slipping that hairy little pooch into the red dog jacket you distribute, or pointing the dog's and owner's noses toward a set of stainless steel collapsible dishes that you just happen to have in your pocket. Try asking Foxie's owner if he's ever tried an Herbal Energy Combo on him. You know just the one. Yes, I'm being a bit flip, but only a bit. Once you start talking dogs (or cats or horses or pigs or African chickens, depending on the animal show you're attending), you can bring up anything you want with the doting owners and they'll listen as long as it pertains to their pet.

6. *Go to any kind of cooking class.* I was with a lady today who says she buys every cookbook that comes out. She says she can't help it. I've found that people who like cookbooks, cooking classes, and food are often jolly, warm types who do well in multilevel. You've probably noticed that when people eat together, camaraderie builds quickly. While chewing on chicken bones and drinking the cooking sherry, I think you'll find it quite easy to start talking your business to a satisfied, beaming, and burping audience.

7. *Go shopping.* Strike up a conversation over the value of different brands of soap. Talking about soap leads to talking about your products. You can stretch from soap to birdseed to water filters. I've said it before, but once you get someone listening or talking to you, you can make wide jumps in the conversation that few people will notice.

8. *Join your kid's PTA.* Go where the people who do things in your community go. They're the ones who know a lot of people, and they're the ones who have the energy to get things done.

9. *Advertise your skills as a handy person, portrait painter, baby sitter, or seamstress in the local paper.* (Or whatever it is that you can do.) People will contact you for your services, and in the performance of those, you'll naturally mention your products and business opportunity.

10. *Find a reason for having your local newspaper print an article about you.* Maybe the reporter's focus will be on the magnificent flowers you grow in your bathtub, but you can get her to mention the multilevel stink-bug-candy business you run on the side.

To get an article, have a good friend or relative call the paper and tell them about this eccentric woman who raises irises in her bathtub. Reporters are always looking for unusual human interest stories.

11. *Join a networking group.* I meet twice a month for breakfast with a group of entrepreneurs like myself. We all promote each other and use each others' services. Women's organizations, professional organizations, networking groups, charity groups, and Chamber of Commerce meetings are all good places to meet people and share your business.

12. *Attach yourself to sales people who come to your door.* Instead of hiding behind the couch when you see them approach, put a "Solicitors Welcome" sign in the window and nab them when they ring the bell. Feed them cake baked in your company's pots and smear them with samples from your cosmetics line. They'll either sign up with you, or put an "X" in front of your house warning all other solicitors to stay clear.

When a telephone solicitor calls, instead of screaming "I don't want any!" and smacking the phone down on the receiver, try another tactic—be nice, and do what I do.

A male telephone solicitor called me. He said that one of my friends gave him my name. (She did, and I was a bit snappish with her, later.) He wanted to sign me up in a dating service, the same one my friend was in. For only $2,000, Carol and I could hunt men together. I was curious to see the setup, because Carol had been regaling me for months with her wild search down there at the dating bureau.

I said I'd be glad to make an appointment with him and his company, but I didn't say that before I'd found out everything I possibly could about him. (I wanted to find out how strong a possibility it was to get him into *my* business before he snagged me into his.)

I asked his name (Tom), and if he'd been telephone soliciting for long. He hadn't. He was fresh from the South, an economics professor, hoping to find work in Southern California. In the meantime, he was having to telephone solicit at five dollars an hour. I asked more questions. I was friendly and interested in him and his life. I asked him if he was happy here, if he'd met people, and what he planned to do next. He started to sound like a real prospect for my business.

I said, "Tell you what. I'm going to send you some samples from the business I do. If you like these and the information I send, you may want to join up with me. There's lotsa' money in it." (I said that because he was, after all, an economics professor.) I ended with, "Give me your address and phone number." He did, without a quibble.

I set an appointment with Tom and the dating service, but I had utterly no intention of joining the group. I'm curious about things and I like to poke around in places and situations, and by the time I met Tom, I figured, he would have tried my samples. I planned to sign him into my business on the spot.

It didn't happen. Tom wasn't there for the meeting. We'd gotten our times mixed up. Instead, the head of the dating service met with me. She was obviously a hardened pro, because in the space of an hour she'd taken pictures of me, had me videotaped, and signed me for $2,000. My credit card slid right out of my hand like it was wired to her fingers.

All I can remember saying is, "But, I don't want to do this, I'm not comfortable with this kind of thing, I'd rather just meet someone naturally. . . ."

The woman countered me with perfect logic, saying things like, "They're never gonna' meet you, you live way out in the country with your dogs and cats and listen sweetheart, time is passing. Look at these lines I've got embedded around my mouth. They weren't here yesterday."

I stumbled out of there, $2,000 lighter, searching with my tongue for those grooves around my lips and thinking, "Well, maybe this is a good thing."

By the end of the week, I felt sure it wasn't. I felt stupid.

I gave Tom a call. Maybe I could salvage some of that money by signing him up.

His brother answered the phone. "Oh, Tom went back to Memphis," he drawled.

"Oh," I said. "Oh, nuts. Did he take those samples I sent him?"

"I don't know, Honey," the brother answered, "he just packed up and left."

I thought about that $2,000. Tom wasn't going anywhere without me. "Can you give me his phone number?" I said. "I really need to talk with him." I got the number.

It felt like my $2,000 had just run off to Memphis. I called him immediately. Tom wasn't there. The old lady who answered said he was out picking peaches. Or maybe he was down at his brother Flint's house. He might not be home for a few days.

"And who are you?" I asked sweetly.

"Why, I'm his Aunt Lilly."

Aunt Lilly sounded nice, and by golly, if I couldn't get Tom, Aunt Lilly was good enough for me. I was going to get that money back, and I just bet Aunt Lilly was ready for multilevel.

"Did Tom share any of those samples with you that I sent him?" I asked.

Aunt Lilly didn't have a dingdong's idea of what I was talking about. I happily filled her in. And, "Yes," she'd, "love to try some, thank you."

I said my usual, "Give me your address, I'll send 'em right down and call you in a few days." And I did.

What follows is common, in one way or another, when you're prospecting, so I might as well continue. This will give you some idea of what to do next, and what can happen.

The conversation with Tom the Telephone Solicitor had first started on December 15th. I sent Aunt Lilly a few samples and some literature on January 11th. I called again on January 16th.

"Did you get the stuff I sent?"

"Yes, I did," she said. "A lot of it's herbs and I don't believe in herbs. I'm trained as a nurse, you know, and this stuff doesn't have the backing of the medical establishment."

"Oh, I understand completely," I continued. "I used to feel the same way myself." (No matter how rude or confusing a prospect is to you, agree with him or her and understand.)

"All vegetables are herbs, you know," I said. "Jesus even talks about them in the Bible." You'll need to be a fast and creative thinker to counter all objections about your products and business. Practice writing answers to all the objections you can think of. That will help when you're not feeling too quick. With Lilly, I believe I got off the subject of herbs and began talking about multilevel. The conversation didn't go too well, but I was charm-

31

ing and understanding and learned all about how to pick and pickle mushrooms. I said I'd call her again the following week.

By the time I called, she'd checked my company out with the FDA and the Better Business Bureau. I told her that I was impressed. I was, too. And, I said I'd call again.

I felt depressed. But, then I thought about that $2,000 that Aunt Lilly was going to make me, and so I called the next week.

Was I lucky. Aunt Lilly had just seen a TV program with a real doctor extolling the merits of herbs. She was mightily impressed. She began taking my products. The next time I called, we had a fine chat about the cat-head embroidered apron she was making, and, wouldn't you know it, she told me that she was the president of the local health chapter for some disease and she was also big in a charity group. (I like people who do things. They're inclined to do MLM, too.)

"Tell you what," I said, "I'm going to send you a copy of my book, *MLM Magic*, and see what you think about multi-level."

Aunt Lilly was as pleased as prunes.

The next time I called, Lilly sounded glad to hear from me. I think I was wearing on her. Both she and her husband had read my book and were now terribly excited about multi-level. In fact, Georgie had just run out and signed up in some oil blending multilevel, and they had me to thank! Great.

I kept calling Aunt Lilly, and eventually I signed her. I think it took about three months. I haven't seen that two thousand dollars, yet, but I may. Meanwhile, Georgie is having a marvelous time with his motor oil multilevel, all thanks to me!

The point of this story is to show you that prospects can be found in the darndest ways, and that once you find a good prospect, you must persist in your pursuit. You have to build relationships. You must turn prospects into people, and people into friends.

Your assignment is to make a list of places and ways to find prospects. This can be fun!

Ways To Find Prospects:

_____

_____

_____

_____

_____

_____

_____

_____

_____

_____

_____

_____

Creating A Prospect List
(See pp. 60-63 in *MLM Magic*.)

While you're thinking about prospects, names of people who need your products and business should come to mind. You will need to keep their names on a list. You can collect them on a sheet or two of paper and immediately lose them, or you can put them in your work journal. Use the page provided in this book as a starting point for listing names. Another idea is to get a small notebook that you dedicate solely for listing prospects in. It should be small enough to keep in your pocket, car, purse, or night stand. In it, write down the names of everyone who needs your product or business. These are people you both know and don't know, people whom you would feel comfortable approaching, and people too far above you to even consider. You should keep the book with you because names will often drop into your head like flies to a barbecue. If you say, "Oh, I'll remember her," or, "I'll write his name down later," you won't. You'll forget. And what if that one person was your retirement, your trip to Bali, or freedom from your cranky mother-in-law in the side house?

Assignment: Write down the names of everyone you can think of who should be using your products. Also write down the names of people who could benefit from being a distributor. You can winnow out and prioritize everyone later.

People Who May Like The Product(s) Or Business Opportunity:

_____

_____

_____

_____

_____

_____

_____

_____

_____

_____

_____

_____

_____

Choosing The Right Prospects
(See pp. 95-114 in *MLM Magic*.)

It may take you a good long while to feel at ease about pinpointing and approaching prospects. Keep practicing, and eventually you'll find that it's easy to find and sign people. Actually, believe it or not, signing people will probably become a simple matter. Then, you'll discover an astounding thing: Most people you sign will be worthless for your purposes.

I know what you may be thinking: Once you sign even one person, or once you learn how to sign many, your retirement is a done deal. Ha! I have a talent for multilevel, yet even I can't make people do what I want them to. I still have trouble deciding who will actually be good at this business. The biggest names in multilevel will tell you that the one person they never thought would do anything is the one who stays and makes them money. And the people they just "knew" would provide them fat royalty checks in their old age to support their decadent life styles are often the ones who flounder and melt away. Why? I don't know. Just know that it's true and you'll feel less suicidal each time it happens.

I can give you lots of ideas and rules to help you choose and sign the right people. Generally, they're good ideas, but you have to remember that you'll never know for sure about someone's suitability until the prospect proves himself out. Eventually, it'll become clear who will work and who will waffle. Here are a few examples from my life to keep you company:

I'm always looking for interesting, sociable people who are go-getters. A few weeks ago, I was in a grocery store line. (This is a good place to look for prospects.) I was a little impatient. It was a long line, filled with droopy looking people, including myself. Suddenly, a man in his early seventies spoke to the woman ahead of me.

"I knew Al Capone," he said.

"You did?" the lady answered.

All of us in the line snapped upright and stared at the fellow. He wore a little straw hat, striped suspenders, and baggy-butt jeans. He looked, with his flushed red face, like a nice country character.

"Yep," he continued. "Knew 'em when I was a kid. Knew all the mobsters. They all wore fancy suits with white carnations in their button holes."

"Oh my," we all gasped. How interesting. A man who actually breathed the same air as famous mobsters. A man who as a little kid talked to them and watched them smoke big cigars that dropped ashes on their shiny suits.

"Yep. One day I asked Mr. Capone something. I said," and he tipped towards us as we all swayed backwards like a line of cornstalks in the wind, "I said, 'Mr. Capone, did you really shoot all those people on Valentine's day?' He laughed and said he sure did."

"Wow," the lady in front of me said.

"Yeah, I was just a kid, hung out with the other kids on the streets of

Chicago. Sometimes we'd see the boys and they'd give us candy."

There was a silence, then he started again, "People don't know this, but during one period, Capone was feeding half of Chicago."

The lady in front of me, speaking for all of us, said crisply, "My. You just don't read about that kind of thing in the papers."

Mr. Suspenders continued to chat as the line crept forward.

"Boy," I thought. "I bet he'd be a good distributor. He's likable, likes to talk, he's not afraid to approach people, and he's certainly old enough to really settle into something."

These thoughts kept circling in my head as the man reached the checker. "Um," I wondered. "Maybe I should speak with him quickly, before he leaves the store."

I opened my mouth, but too late, he was now addressing the checker.

"You know," he said loudly, as he leaned toward her but faced us, his attentive audience, "last week, it was all over the news, so you probably know, Jesus Christ gave the president six million dollars to put toward the national debt."

The whole line of us sank back to our droopy postures, sliding back on our heels while giving each other the old eyerolls.

Thank heaven. He was one less prospect I had to approach. It's nice when a person let's you know right off like that that they're completely unsuitable. Usually, you don't figure out for weeks or months that you've signed someone up who's totally unsuitable. What normally happens is that you find someone who talks well, looks good, makes sense, promises you everything, and then drops out.

For example, I once signed a man after many phone calls, faxes, and product samples. Two months later, he told me, "I don't have any money to buy products, my wife and kids are totally against what I'm doing, and I'm not sure I like your products."

He'd also told me along the way that he'd lost his job,

was involved in another multilevel, and had a personality disorder.

I never had much confidence that he'd do anything, so I wasn't upset or surprised when he said he was quitting. I suspected that he was much too busy fighting with his wife and kids and his personality disorder to even attempt to climb the other hills he had in front of him. So why did I even bother with him? I liked him, and he seemed to want a chance. It didn't hurt me to give it to him. Would I suggest you spend time with a prospect like this in the first place? No. Or, only marginally. Unfortunately, many people involved in multilevel unwittingly prospect people like this fellow and then spend *all* their time and hope on them.

Here are a few more unlikely prospects:

When Billy Jim said to me, "I never follow through on anything, but I will on this," I immediately took my heart out of the conquest. People tend to repeat their patterns. I learned this lesson in love, and I've carried it over into my business life. If a man tells you he's a bad guy, has a lurid past with women, and advises you not to fall in love with him, he means it. Listen carefully to what people tell you about themselves.

When I called Patti and she said, "I didn't get my money sent to the company for my distributor application. Something came up. There was a class I was taking and my paper was due and late. I'll sign eventually, but I don't want to have to use these products forever," I knew she wouldn't do the business, and correctly gathered that she would never sign up. Again, listen carefully to what people say, and read between the lines when you have to.

My last example of a bad prospect is Todd. He was out of work and trying to build two multilevels at the same time. He'd heard of me and my company, and he wanted to join up. I advised him to choose just one company and stick with it. After some thought, he chose mine. He called me three and four times a day with questions, which delighted me. He was serious. But oddly enough, he couldn't make it to any meetings, even though he planned to buy a large amount of product and begin at a high level of operation. After about a month, he called and told me he couldn't afford to do my multilevel, that for some reason he had to do the other two. It didn't make any sense to me, but I understood. I understood that he'd always been confused, and I wasn't surprised at the confusing outcome.

An example of a good prospect is Celeste. She took my products and loved them. She's single, a grandma, and a bit lonesome. She has a part-time job, but she needs more money. She signed up and comes to every meeting and every seminar. She calls me often. She likes to come and visit with me. She tends to overlook company foul-ups and late orders. She has ups and downs while building this business, but she understands them and recovers. She's steady. She's kind of dull. No crises, you know. She'll eventually bring the money in nice and comfortably for both of us.

I was slow to get interested in Celeste, and now I have to remind myself to work with her. Why? Because she wasn't gaudy and free-wheeling, she didn't appear to be someone who'd grab this business and run with it. But she's just the kind of person you should look for and work with. Remember this when flamboyant flakes are flying through your life.

Here's a list that may help you sort people. How many qualifications does your prospect have?

- The prospect has past MLM experience.
- Loves your products.
- Is a woman.
- Is a self-starter.
- Is determined to make this business work, recognizes the opportunity, and will seriously commit to working the multilevel.
- Is a steady worker.
- Has a positive outlook and is open-minded and happy.
- Wants more out of life.
- Wants freedom, flexibility, and mobility.
- Has lots of social contacts.
- Does things for his or her community.
- Has had jobs where she has displayed initiative—she gets out and finds business. e.g. in sales, real estate, insurance, etc.
- Is entrepreneurial.
- Is a teacher.
- Takes calculated risks and makes own decisions.
- Is not a complainer. Is a problem-solver.
- Has a healthy self image.
- Likes competition.
- Sets goals.
- Is creative.

- Is persistent.
- Completes what she starts.
- Loves people.
- Is a dysfunctional type who has recovered or is well on the way to recovery.
- Is an older person.
- Is desperate.

To make it more complicated, there's always the person who you think will never make it—and who does.

Assignment: Look at your prospect list and see if you can tell what qualities each person has. Don't expect to always be right. Contact everyone on your list who seem at all likely, and give each of them a chance. Then watch and listen to them, *between the lines*, as they show and tell you all about themselves.

Your Prospect Notebook

Once you've found some likely prospects (people you're actually working on and with), you need to keep track of them.

Use one of your three-ring binders or a spiral notebook. Write *Prospects* on the front. Put all your prospects, *one to a page*, in there with as much information about them as you can gather, starting with name, address, and phone number. Mark down every time you talk to them and what was said. Note any product or material you sent or gave to them. Keep this notebook close to you or your phone so you can add information as it comes in.

If and when these prospects graduate to distributors, pull their page out and put it in a plastic page protector (these are available at office supply stores). You'll use plastic because you'll be handling that page a lot as you help this person build a business. Peanut butter, garden mud, or cat pee won't hurt plastic. Put that page of information in a binder or a colored folder marked *Distributors*. Go through this folder every couple of days and call these people or do whatever is necessary. Take notes on the various sheets about what transpires.

When and if a distributor graduates to manager, supervisor, Diamond Toad-Head, or whatever title your company uses to indicate a higher level, put the person in another colored folder marked with the corresponding rank. Call the person every day or so, send her the latest information, invite her to fascinating functions, etc. (Just don't make a nuisance of yourself or make her wish you'd lose your voice. Be sensitive.)

At this point in my business life, I like keeping people in colored folders. Folders are easy to sling around on my kitchen table, or to take to the bedroom when I want to lie down on the job and call people. When I'm concentrating on one person, I can simply pull out their plastic page and work with it.

Assignment: Set up this system, or create your own way to keep everyone in their proper category. Write down your ideas here, and make a shopping list for folders to buy.

Ideas For Categorizing My Prospects, Etc.

_____

_____

_____

_____

_____

_____

_____

_____

_____

_____

_____

How To Approach A Prospect

(See pp. 78-89 in *MLM Magic*.)

Many people are terrorized at the thought of talking to a stranger about their products or business. To put it in perspective, I think it's much more dangerous to talk to your relatives about your new business. They feel free to attack and trounce you for your stupidity, but strangers are much more polite.

Here's how I approach people, and the steps I follow afterwards:

1. Be friendly. Start chatting with someone in a grocery store or movie theater line.

"Nice day, isn't it?" (You don't have to be profound, just friendly.) If you're real nervy, you might say something like, "Is that your real hair?" or, "I have a funny looking kid too." (Just teasing!) After the small talk, you might say, "Do you like your phone service?" or, "Do you take herbs?" Say anything that halfway relates to your business. You're turning the conversation down your side of the street.

Ease into your product announcements. For example, let's say you have a great weight loss program.

"I've discovered the best way to lose weight," you say casually. "You'd never believe that last year I weighed 280 pounds, all below my waist."

If all goes according to plan, the other person's eyebrows get stuck at their hairline as they whisper, "You did? What happened to it?"

That's your cue. Now you can reveal your product.

The idea is to dream up creative ways to mention your product or business without having the prospect feel like you're about to shoot him with the Opportunity Of A Lifetime.

Your assignment is to think of and write down creative ways to mention your products or business to a prospect.

_____

_____

_____

_____

_____

_____

_____

_____

_____

_____

_____

_____

_____

_____

_____

_____

_____

2. Be prepared. Always carry your little prospect notebook and a sample of your products. Ask for the other person's card, or write down their name, address, and phone number. If the person seems receptive, pull a crumpled sample out of your pocket, shake it out and say, "I'll call tomorrow and see how you like the stuff." You could add, "Well, there's a business opportunity attached to this. Do you have a few minutes?"

A lot of people who teach multilevel or fancy they're a hot shot in it would blanch at this approach. It works for me because I'm so casual that no one knows what I'm up to. Just happening to have a loose sample in my pocket is a lot less threatening to someone then being hustled by a super salesperson who's out to sell you everything he's got in his car or the back bedroom. And even setting up a real appointment for a business presentation makes people suspicious and nervous. It's like waiting to see the dentist.

For example, I went to a franchising and multilevel business convention a few days ago. Even though I paid $7 and knew what I was in for, I was only able to stomach twenty minutes. If I looked a salesperson in the eye, they grabbed me. Everyone was offering free samples and trying to drag me into their seminars. "Just sign here and write down your phone number and the best time to call." I got a headache and an upset stomach. Sometimes people in multilevel act like they are hawkers at one of these shows. People hate it.

Assignment: Write down ideas for samples or literature or fun things you can give to people.

_____

_____

_____

_____

_____

_____

_____

_____

_____

_____

_____

_____

3. Follow through. A few nights ago, I was at a dinner theater, high up in the piney, frosty mountains. There were nine of us all huddled at a wooden table, alternately freezing and roasting as an old heater sporadically spit warm air from the ceiling. We were covered with grease, eating barbecued meat, beans, and potato salad as we laughed and talked about our lives and gossiped about people at the table next to us. Somehow, multilevel came up, and I was astonished to find that everyone at the table was involved in one. The only dissident was a man who had been in a multilevel before and who said that the experience was enough to hold him for a lifetime. Then someone else said, "The part I hate the most, the part I just can't do, is picking up that phone!"

Trudy, the dark-haired lady across from me who bakes twenty dozen different kinds of cookies every Christmas, said, "If I have a shop and they come to me, I can sell 'em anything. Anything! I'm a born salesperson. But if I have to call and hustle them? I can't do it."

The man at the end of the table shook his head. "I love my multilevel," he said. "I'd rather be doing that than my computer business." He made a sour face, "But I hate making calls, too."

Everybody looked at me.

"I like making calls," I said.

Clearly, they thought I fibbed.

I know how they felt. I used to feel the same way. After I'd written up my long list of prospects when first starting my current multilevel, I kind of collapsed. I was sitting on my bed with this huge list in my hand. I leaned back and slowly slid down onto the bed. I thought, "Oh no. I'm going to have to call all these people."

I made myself do it. I knew these people didn't want to talk to me about multilevel. Many were rude and some just barely contained their boredom or irritation. What kept me dialing my old rotary princess telephone was this thought: "These people need these products. These people need this business. I love and believe in these products and this business. I'm desperate and I have to do this, or I will always be poor."

Those same thoughts kept me going when I had to call prospects I'd just met.

Trust me. The more you do it, the easier it gets.

When you call a person, ask if he can talk. He'll hate you right off if you don't, and you happened to beep through on call-waiting, or while he's eating dinner, or making love, or watching the ending of a great movie.

Once he says "okay" though, be friendly and warm. Act and feel like he's a great friend of yours. He is. He's a part of you, another human being. Don't be insincere.

Also, get right to the point. Say, "The reason I'm calling is because. . . etc." I get annoyed when people call me, ask how I am, what I'm doing, how my daughter is, say they've been thinking of me, they've missed me, and then twenty minutes later they say, "Oh, by the way, I want something from you."

The next day, call again and ask the person if he's thought about what you've said. Or, send him a brochure with more information or send a sample of your product(s) while you get your nerves settled down, then call again in two or three days.

Say something like, "Did you try that stuff? Not yet? Give it a try. I'll call tomorrow and see if your life has changed!" or, "What did you think? Well, if you like it I can get you some." (Never say "I can *sell* it to you." *Get* always sounds better than *sell*.) Invite the person to come over at two p.m. tomorrow to pick up the product or say, "I'm going by your place tomorrow afternoon—I'll drop it off, okay?"

Another approach might be to say, "Why don't I run by and we can chat about this. I'm on my way to the cleaners, it'll just take a minute."

Assignment: Write down different things you can say when you connect with a prospect on the phone. Also, write down what you can say to a prospect whom you've already met. Think up different scenarios.

_____

_____

_____

_____

_____

_____

_____

_____

_____

_____

_____

_____

_____

_____

_____

_____

4. Instead of calling someone off your prospect list, you can always write a letter first. Send a nice, informal, friendly, *handwritten* note about what you've just discovered and why you're writing to the person. Maybe put *one* brochure inside. Say you'll call in a few days. (Don't expect anyone to yell "Yippee! Eureka! God is good! He's sent us a multilevel, the answer to our prayers, let's call Ruthie right away!") You'll have to call the person.

As for the letter being handwritten, many people say, "That'll take me forever, with all these people on my list!"

I tell them, "Okay. Type a master letter and print it out. Nobody will feel special, but you can add a handwritten note to it. That will help. But since you're going to do the work anyway, and you *are* trying to build a business, why don't you do something that has the most chance of working? Why waste your time on a letter that no one will read?"

Assignment: Write a handwritten letter.

5. Offer an opportunity, if the time seems right. Maybe you didn't mention the business part before because you sensed your prospect would have gone leery and cagey on you. But now, they really do like your stuff and seem ready to tell their friends about it. (This is where it's important to have a good product. Don't get involved with anything that you don't believe in.) At this point, bring up the business opportunity involved. Think of it as a chance to help your friend, and yourself, too.

Assignment: Write out different ways to mention your business opportunity. If you're tired of writing, try tape recording different approaches to see how you sound. Have your willing husband, wife, kid, or dog listen to you and give rebuttals. They'll be happy to find the flaws!

_____

_____

_____

_____

_____

_____

_____

_____

_____

_____

_____

_____

6. Present the opportunity. After you mention the business opportunity to your prospect and you get a positive response, it's time to present the opportunity and invite your prospect to a meeting. There are many ways of doing this. You can invite your prospect to meet with you one-on-one, or you can invite her to a home meeting or a company-sponsored meeting.

Most importantly, you need to give her some detailed information about the company's products and marketing plan. You can do all of this over the phone, but it's more difficult that way. So setting up a meeting is important. But try to avoid using the word *meeting*. People hate meetings. They've had bad experiences with them. See what else you can come up with. A *potluck, tea party, get-together, meet-the-new-neighbors party,* or even *lunch* sounds a whole lot better than inviting someone to a *meeting*. Be honest, however, about what this get together is about and what you'll do there. If people think they're coming for beer and a food fight and you sit them down for two hours explaining how they'll become millionaires selling sequin jackets for turtles through multilevel, expect those folks to be mad at you later.

A distributor of mine, Brenda, is very good at giving presentations. Her idea was to start her business by having luncheons in her home. She invited friends who brought friends and everyone contributed a potluck dish and left the kids at home. Brenda manipulated the party just a bit so practically all they talked about was her new business and the stories about her products. At the end of every lunch, she'd say, "If you like what you've heard, come back the first Tuesday of every month and bring your friends."

As the months danced along and Brenda's friends and friends of friends became distributors, they outgrew Brenda's home. Brenda's little lunches had to move to a hotel.

Your assignment is to plan an interesting or unusual get-together where you can showcase your products and business opportunity to all your prospects.

_____

_____

_____

_____

_____

_____

_____

_____

_____

_____

_____

7. Take your new person to a large company meeting. As soon as your prospect is involved with the product and interested in learning more, take him to a big company meeting when one comes to your area. Arrange to pick up and drive your prospect, so you both get there.

8. Keep in Touch: Whether the person becomes a retail customer, prospect, or distributor, keep calling. Some of us find this difficult. Remember, you're here to help these people lead a better life with your products or opportunity. Tell your new friends you'll keep up with them unless they tell you to knock it off. Keep a sense of humor.

(For more ideas and information on finding prospects, order my booklet and audio, *Prospecting,* from Ransom Hill Press. 1-800-423-0620)

5

Training Your Distributors

(See pp. 132-136 in *MLM Magic*.)

I've seen lots of people who feel so relieved when they've finally signed someone that they don't go any farther. The sponsor forgets that the new person is probably not like him or herself and won't do anything unless taught how to do it.

It's important to give new distributors a lot of time and your fondest attention. You need to counsel and train them.

Training distributors takes a lot of hand-holding and support. The success of your business depends on the success of your distributors. Here are four things you can do immediately to start training your distributors:

• **Don't procrastinate!** Get all the appropriate information to your new person immediately, and teach him to do the same for his distributors.

• **Call each distributor often.** (Every day? Three times a week?) Or, better yet, train your person to call *you* daily to check in.

• **Teach your people how to sign three to five good frontline people.** Make sure they teach these people to do the same.

• **Teach them how to write and run ads if that seems appropriate.**

Also, continuously ask your upline to help you with your new distributors. Ask your upline to call your new distributors and introduce themselves and offer to be available for answering tough questions, to speak at their in-home meetings, and to just be there for general support. Think of your upline as grandparents to your distributors. They will surely help you, since your upline's success is dependent on your success and the success of your distributors.

What You Must Ask From Your New Distributors Immediately

(See pp. 126-132 in *MLM Magic*.)

• Get a commitment to the business from each of them as soon as you sign them up.

• Have them make wish lists just like the wish list you made when you started your business. Remember, that's a list of what they each want their multilevel business to get for them.

• Have them acquire enough product to get started. This should be minimal. Some companies and some multilevel people see this differently. It's true, some folks can order cases and cases of product and build a magnificent fortune almost overnight. However, I find that most people aren't that able, right away. You don't want to demand too much and throw your new person into debt and despair. Slow and steady and true are better than fast and flash and cinder.

• Get a no-squirm-out promise from your new distributor to attend the next meeting or training session that's in town. Pick her up to make sure she gets there.

• Have your new distributors make prospect lists just like you made yours.

• Have each of them set up an event with the people on their prospect lists. Help each distributor arrange a pot luck, tea party, etc. Make the business opportunity meeting into something fun. *You* need to attend every get-together too, and help your distributors with their prospects.

• Have each new distributor set up personal appointments with his or her prospects. These can be formal, or more like I do: I usually just "run into" people, give them a little talk wherever I find them, then do a follow-up call or note, then more follow-up. People hate to be chased down and cornered, so make any appointments you set seem casual.

• Remind your new distributors of the importance of reading all the books and listening to all the audios on MLM that you have available for them. Tell them to think of this as "job training" for their new field.

• Draw up a blueprint for each new distributor. A blueprint is a map that outlines how a distributor will build his business. This blueprint will encourage him, make the marketing plan more clear, and help him get started. Write the steps out for him.

Also ask your new distributor, "How much money do you need or want to make per month from this opportunity?" When you get a total, map out how he can make that kind of money in your company. For example, if your distributor wants to make $8,000 a month, figure up how many cases or bottles or buckets of product would have to move through his downline to reach that objective.

Your assignment is to draw up a blueprint for yourself.

_____

_____

_____

_____

_____

_____

_____

_____

_____

_____

_____

Checklist For New Distributors

(See p. 136 in *MLM Magic*.)

Here's a checklist that you might consider typing up, copying, and handing to each new distributor that you sign.

- Commit to the business.
- List what you want the business to do for you.
- Order product.
- Make a prospect list.
- Attend company-sponsored meetings and training meetings given by upline.
- Get an answering machine.
- Study MLM training materials in your company's distributor kit, plus any audios, videos, or books about multilevel that you can find.
- Practice calling people.
- Learn how to do a presentation.
- Give a home meeting. Learn how to sign up people.
- Consider getting an 800 number if you have out of the area distributors. (And only if you can afford it.)
- Carry product in your car.
- Go through *The MLM Magic Workbook*.

My Daily Plan

(See pp. 145-147 in *MLM Magic*.)

When I first started building my business. I had a "real" job, but I worked at home. Plus, I had only one teenager. I had it easier than some of you. I didn't have a nine to five job two hours away on the freeway and I didn't have a pile of little kids pulling at my pantlegs and throwing up on my papers.

Whatever your situation, you'll have to make adjustments that suit your place in life. Just remember, you can do anything you want to do. If you want your freedom badly enough, you will figure out how to work around all your current impediments.

For example, today I had lunch with one of my downline, Ellie. She was perplexed, saying, "Most of my distributors have full-time jobs and some have little kids, Venus. How can they work this business?"

I said, "I'd be up before the kids, doing whatever MLM work could be done at that hour. During my lunch break I'd be calling people or writing letters, and I'd do whatever I could after the kids went to bed. I'd also make most of my phone calls on Saturdays. That's when people are home, anyway. They're also not watching the news or eating dinner, so a call won't annoy them.

"And," I reminded my friend, "when I first started my business, I shoved all my manuscripts under the bed. I knew I wouldn't be able to work on them until I was making enough money to do so—without guilt, anyway."

"That's right!" Ellie shouted. "I used to make patchwork quilts. I put those away until I got my business going, too. Now, I'm working on them again."

I agreed, saying, "Your downline will just have to put some important or fun things aside until there's time for them, later."

Here was my typical day when I was building my multilevel business:
7:00 a.m.

I'm showered, dressed, I've had my tea and quiet thinking or happy reading time, and am now in my kitchen office.

If I can think of anyone to call this early, I will. I keep in mind, though, that some people are three hours ahead of or behind me. I'm sensitive to this, because people who call me often forget it. I've had a number of calls at 4:00 a.m.

One man in Australia called me at 2:30 a.m. I said, "It's 2:30 a.m. here."

He said, "Oh really, mate? Well, listen. I have a man here. I want you to talk to him. I've read your books and I want you to just chat with 'em a bit and get 'em interested in multilevel for me." Very nervy.

The 4:00 a.m. callers will generally rip right into their talk about what a marvelous multilevel they're involved in—and they know I'll want to hear all about it! Not at 4:00 a.m., I don't. Not even at 6:00 a.m.

Yes, people call me at 6:00 a.m. too. They figure that since they're up and at it, I should be too. There's one lady who specializes in 6:00 a.m. calls. Sometimes, I'm not quite up yet, or I'm busy thinking. The last time she did this I said to her, "I'm in bed. I'm asleep." She didn't skip a word or even pause. This kind of thing doesn't further your cause with your prospects.

If I'm not making calls, I'm planning out the day and writing it down.

Maybe I'm writing up a newsletter too, or a new, informative flyer.

8:00 a.m.

As the day progresses, I fit in breakfast. Sometimes I rearrange and clean up my work area. Other times, I attempt to remember everyone I ever knew so I can write or call each of them about my new business.

9:00 a.m. to noon

I call my downline, or they call me, and we set up times to get together, or we discuss their key people and how we can help them.

Sometimes, if I feel like giving a different kind of ad another shot, I write the ad. Maybe it's one specifically for my business, or maybe it's the kind I prefer, where I'm advertising for my counseling business in order to get clients and prospects. Or, I may listen to a training tape, watch a company video for inspiration, or read a multilevel or sales book. I think it's wise to listen to or watch or read something everyday that inspires me to build the business.

If I have ad calls coming in at a certain time, I stay home and wait for them, or I redo the recorded message I have while waiting for callers.

Sometimes I sit outside and think about what working in this multilevel will do for me, and what I can do next to build it better.

12:00 noon to 1:30 p.m.

Sometimes I take a prospect to lunch. When I'm buying, he or she can't complain about what I talk about. . .and I talk business.

I might plan a home meeting with some of my downline for their new prospects and mine. I might work right through lunch, which I don't think is right or healthy.

1:30 to 7:00 p.m.

Some days I go people hunting. That might mean grocery, clothes, or window shopping, or I may sit at an outside coffee shop or on a wooden chair in a mall and watch people. If someone sits down beside me or gets too close, I start talking to him. Most of the time, no business comes of it, but I have a happy time, and I'm getting myself more socialized and at ease with people.

I may send postcards to my downline to keep them inspired, or call a retail buyer to see how well they liked the product.

At least every other day I'll call my upline's voice mailbox to hear about new developments in the company, or information on local meetings. Or, I'll call one of my upline for encouragement and gossip. Sometimes I'll even call someone else's upline. I want to absorb and be around success.

7:00 p.m.

Tonight might be a Mexican do at Theresa's house with our products mixed in with the hot sauce.

Of course, I go to every meeting and class that anyone in my company lets me come to. I'll drive miles for a drop of knowledge. I'll even go to other company's meetings to see how they operate, although this is tricky. You want to stay one-pointed in the MLM of your choice.

Maybe I'm in bed by eleven, but it's with a book in hand. Usually it's something that will help me with my business, or help me grow as a person. Generally, I'm so absorbed in my work and plans that I dream about the business all night!

That was my typical twenty-four hours that I worked around my other home job. Are you willing to do all that for two to three years or more, to earn your freedom for life?

6

Meetings

Checklist For Meetings

(See pp. 149-153 in *MLM Magic*.)

Whatever you call them—meetings, potlucks, pool parties, get-togethers, or discussions, here are a few ideas that will help you build your business this way:

1. Choose the right day and time. Tuesday through Thursday nights are the best. Saturday during the day can be good too. Maybe you'll call it an open house, a potluck, a card or tea party. Let your prospects know it's a business meeting, too. People don't like to be tricked. Tell them you have a wonderful opportunity you want to share. If they ask what it is, tell them. Be honest and up-front. You want their trust and you don't want them to toss you out of their house or race out of yours when the truth comes out.

2. Call your prospects and distributors. Use food, guilt, or elaborate promises (none you can't keep) to get them there. Get a commitment.

3. Get your upline to be there to help you run the meeting and eat your food.

4. Call your prospects and distributors again the day before or the day of the meeting. Say, "Oh golly, Joan, I'm counting on you to be there." If you ask each person to bring something important (like the weenies), everyone will feel they have to show, or nobody will eat.

5. Start on time. Most of us dislike waiting for the latecomers. It puts us in a bad mood right off and we're annoyed with the host/hostess and the late folk. This naturally extends to a bad feeling for whatever the business opportunity might be.

6. Ask for names and ask attendees to say why they're there. Some will say they're crazy about your products, others will mention that they're

59

looking for a great business opportunity or say that they're curious. (Some of those folk will be your coached upline.) Be prepared, however, to hear some shocking truths like, "My wife made me come," or, "You said I had to be here or you wouldn't go golfing with me Thursday," or, "I just came to eat."

7. Describe your company products and story.

8. Show a video or play an audio.

9. Hand out samples.

10. Encourage your upline or other people to tell their miraculous stories about your business and products.

11. Offer the business opportunity.

12. Ask if anyone sees an opportunity for him or herself.

13. Work with those that see the opportunity, and let the others eat your cookies and run.

14. Sign up those who are willing.

15. The most important suggestion here is to not *bore* anybody. I have been to some terrible meetings in my life. I've felt stuck and stapled to my chair while the speaker dragged on and on or the video ground along for an hour. I sag and sigh especially loudly when people start swishing numbers around on the blackboard and solemnly state, "If five people sign up five people who sign up five people who sign up five, who sign up five more, you have just signed up all of China and are making a million a week—and friends, this is quite possible and easy to do."

In Real Life, I haven't seen that numbers thing work out yet. Keep your meetings very, very simple, and believable.

Here's a flyer that I did up for a tea party meeting. This tea party was a bit different from my in-home teas where we drink tea, eat cakes, and talk about business, romance, men, fantasies, and money, all mixed up together.

You are invited to a Tea Party!

Featuring: Passion Fruit Tea, English Scones, and a real Tea Leaf Reader.

Have you wished you could meet more women like yourself? That you could make good friends in town to have tea with and nice chats? Now you can!
Thursday August 19th—7pm-9pm
@ Jacob's at 424 Main St.

Hosts & Hostesses will be:

MARSHA LIBBENS—She will give everyone a complimentary Hair Styling Consultation. (Is it time to color, perm, or highlight your hair??)
VENUS ANDRECHT— Internationally known Author and Herbalist will discuss herbs, natural health, and effective and long lasting weight loss and maintenance strategies. She will also give personal consultations.
JIMMY McWHORTER, JR. and JOHN WAGNER—Both will provide complimentary scientific body fat analysis.
MARGARET McWHORTER—Well known Tea Leaf Reader with more than thirty years of experience.

Bring your friends! Men welcome, too.
For more information call: 788-0000.

You'll notice the tea leaf reader is my mother, Jimmy is my brother, John is my boyfriend, and the hair stylist is Jimmy's friend.

How did this "meeting" work out? It was a smash as a party. People even came in off the street and ate our scones, passion fruit tea, and samples of products. In fact, they scoured the platters clean. Everyone lolled around and got their fat tested, moaned and whined about the results, went in and ate more scones with cream and blackberry jam, said what a great party it was, and left. We didn't sell a thing or sign anybody up.

My brother Jimmy quit the business immediately afterward and drifted back into restaurant work, John gave it up shortly thereafter, and the hair stylist was never heard from again.

But, like I said, everybody came, and we even had party crashers. If I were to do it again, though, I'd set it up so people had to listen to a talk or watch a video while they ate. Or, in order to eat, they'd have to listen to me first. You know, like they do at fairs. Haven't most of us hovered around the guy who's frying up chicken and vegetables in his fancy priced wok because we know we'll get a dab of it in the end? (Usually after a thirty minute sales pitch.) We'll wait for fudge samples, pizza, or even chopped carrots. We endure all kinds of torture and boredom as we hang around like beady eyed chickens waiting for a feed.

At my party, while folks were getting their fat pinched, someone should have been there to explain what kind of weight loss program they needed, and fed them samples of it after they had listened, spell-bound and drooling, for awhile.

All your meetings, and maybe even most of them, like mine, won't be total or even partial successes. That's okay. Learn from them.

Your assignment is to make an outline for a meeting you'll give.

_____

_____

_____

_____

_____

_____

_____

_____

_____

_____

_____

One-On-One Meetings, A.K.A. *Presentations.*

(See p. 153 in *MLM Magic.*)

1. Go through your prospect list.
2. Prioritize the people in order of who you think needs the product or business most.
3. Call those people you just prioritized.
4. Set up appointments to tell them more about it.
5. Send a postcard to each person to remind them.
6. If someone cancels, reschedule her right away.
7. At your appointment, present the products or opportunity. Be friendly and fun. Be a real person.
8. Ask questions about the person so you'll know how to explain your outstanding opportunity to them on a personal level.

9. Close the sale. "Would you like a bottle of this? I can get you some. It's in my car," or, "Do you see an opportunity here? Do you feel comfortable or interested in this? Here's where you sign to be a distributor. What do you want to do?"

Deliberately setting up appointments for one-on-ones the way I've just described to you makes me uncomfortable. I mention them here because some people like them and because "everybody" says you're supposed to do them this way. But I figure if you know both "their" way *and* "my" way, you'll settle on *your* way.

Let me tell you about one of the few prearranged one-on-ones I've done and you'll see why I don't care for them.

Bonzo was a car salesman. He seemed like a nice fellow. He sold me the Volvo I got for my daughter, Summer. He was personable and warm and laughed at all my jokes. I told him (honestly), that I had to get Summer a Volvo because she needed an extremely safe car. I explained that I was doing it for me, not her, and that I needed peace of mind about her safety. I mentioned that while taking her driving test, she immediately drove over the curb. The man passed her because he assumed she was just nervous. She wasn't. She always drives over the curb.

Anyway, one thing led to another. I wanted to dance into my multilevel act right there, but I couldn't because his boss was too attentive to our conversation. To humor me, I suppose, since I was spending so much money with him, he let me set an appointment to come to his house and show him this great opportunity that would yank him out of car sales.

The appointment was for the following week, at 7:30 at night in the wintertime, forty-five minutes from my home.

First of all, I'm a day girl. I love to be out while the sun is rolling around in the sky, but once it's down, that's it for me. I set when the sun does.

But the following week there I was, out after dark, alone, cold, and nervous. I'd had time to think about what I was going to say and do.

I got lost. Lost in the dark. Finally, I found the street, but I couldn't see the house numbers. Eventually, I chose a house and pulled over. Then I snatched up my pile of products, brochures, and the company presentation binder. I advanced toward the house, dropping papers all the way. As I inched up the steps I felt like a door-to-door salesperson approaching someone who was probably eating dinner in their underpants or watching the only Lassie show that would never be shown in the free world again.

I rang the bell. Bonzo's wife let me in. Nada looked at me like, "How long are you going to stay here? My husband and I have been fighting all week about this."

I grinned and flapped my arms and hands like a marionette, trying to be likable. My papers and products fell in flutters and thumps at Nada's feet.

After an agonizing fifteen minutes of small talk and my mandatory cooing and drooling over their two teensy screaming tots, we settled in the living room. Bonzo and his wife sat on the couch. One of them had artfully placed me two miles across a fallen tree table from them, in a cane chair that poked my butt. The teensy screaming tots stayed up with us and cried and slithered across the table top and into all my papers, products, and the suddenly amazingly complicated company marketing plan. Periodically, the little mighty ones yanked my hair, bounced on my lap with their sharp little feet, and took every opportunity to direct the conversation towards them or the dogs they suspected I had at home.

After an hour, I gave up and left.

One-on-ones by accident are much easier. I present the products or opportunity wherever I find someone. For example, I'm in a hotel retail shop, standing in a post office line, or exchanging conversation with people at another table in a restaurant. We're chatting, and the person shows an interest in something I've said that can be even loosely relevant to my business. I might say, "Do you have a minute? Let's sit down, I'll show you something," or I'll just say or show them whatever I want as we're speaking.

As an example, I was talking with a fellow from England the other day. I hadn't just run into him, I'd met him the day before. I was biding my time. Our conversation shifted to his grandmum.

"She was wide as a boat," he said, "and never wore 'er teeth. I loved 'er. After she died, it was a funny thing. She started comin' back to me. I've never seen 'er, but I smell 'er."

"Really?" I said. I love this kind of thing. "What do you mean?"

"Well," he continued, "she lived with a yeast factory on one side 'o her and a brewery on the other. Now, when she comes to me, I smell yeast and beer so strong, along with her coal burnin' stove! It's such a comfort. I feel happy for days after."

After I finished laughing about the signatures of her presence, I whipped out a sample of one of my products and said, "This'll make you feel happy all the time and you won't have to wait to smell beer and yeast!"

I know. That's stretching it, but, I've told you, I slip what I want into a conversation, any way I can. You can do the same. Try it. Nobody seems to notice the way the conversation has escaped.

Another thing I like to do is swing by some place where I know someone, maybe even just slightly, and say, "Hi Joe, can you take a coffee break? I want to show you something."

Of course, if you're contacting people off your prospect list, it's difficult to be so spur of the moment and casual. With those people, I generally use the same tone with them on the phone or through the mail that I use with a person I've just run into. However, I announce the reason for my call right away. Sometimes I say, "Let's have coffee and talk about this some more," or, "Can I run over and show you this stuff, rub some on your face, hook it up to all your spigots, drop off a tape, watch a video with you, etc.? I'm going that way, anyhow. It'll just take a minute."

Your assignment is to think about and list all the ways you might react and the things you might say and do in an informal presentation.

_____

_____

_____

_____

_____

_____

_____

_____

_____

_____

_____

7

Advertising

Sample Ads

(See pp. 165-171 in *MLM Magic.*)

Many people feel they must advertise in order to build a multilevel. I think everybody tries it. Some people are naturals at it, but, I suspect most of us aren't. As I mentioned earlier, my most successful ads are when I advertise for a service I perform. Then, in the process of performing it, I happen to mention my products or opportunity.

Writing an ad is not as simple as you may think. You need to be specific about what you want. If you're writing a regular multilevel ad, looking for distributors, ask for someone with certain attributes that you have found are useful to a distributor. For example, state that you're looking for someone with experience selling real estate or insurance. Ask for a self-starter. Teachers are good. I used to only ask for someone currently employed because I wanted a stable sort of person. Now, the economy isn't stable and many people don't have jobs who ordinarily would.

While writing your ad, be cautious of luring people with mysterious references to "a fortune at your fingertips," or that type of thing. Most of us are leery of that kind of ad. Remember, you're hoping to attract a neat person like yourself. What would attract you?

Read the ads in the MLM newspapers and regular newspapers. (To find them, look under "sales" or "business opportunities.") Note the ones that sound inviting. Ads that tell you about the products or the company are a novelty, I think, because many people don't mention them. I've heard other multilevel big shots say, "But, if you tell them, they won't call." In my way of thinking, that's one less person you'll have to waste your time with.

This was one of my best ads: "Person with MLM experience, sales, teaching, or managerial background to introduce products that are breaking all international sales records. Must be capable of handling exceptionally large incomes. Only those currently employed need apply. [In these times, when many capable people are out of work, this line could be changed.] Call Ms. Andrecht at 619-788-0000."

Don't make your offer too general, and for you own sake, start with a small ad in a fairly small paper. I got a call from a man who put a half-page ad in the National Enquirer. He was so overwhelmed with responses he couldn't handle them all and frantically called me to find out what to do next. He just wasn't prepared. Be ready before you launch a major ad campaign.

Some people like to advertise their products, not the business opportunity. If you do this, make whatever you sell sound interesting. Most people copy whatever everyone else does and life gets dull. If writing is not your forte, ask someone who has the talent to help you write up an ad.

Your assignment is to cut various multilevel business and product ads out of newspapers and magazines. Paste them in this Workbook.

Now, practice writing your own multilevel or product ads. See how much more clever and interesting you can make yours. Remember, simplicity is always best. Let yourself be wild and nutty for awhile. You don't have to use these samples, but the practice will loosen you up, and something valuable might pop out.

_____

_____

_____

_____

_____

_____

_____

_____

_____

_____

_____

_____

Now, write some sample ads featuring one or several of your talents or hobbies. Remember, these will bring people into your life. That's why you're advertising—to find more people.

_____

_____

_____

_____

_____

_____

_____

_____

_____

_____

_____

8

Newsletters and Mailing Lists

Sample Newsletter

(See pp. 172-179 in *MLM Magic*.)

Many of my downline have said to me, "The only reason I'm still with you and this business is because of your newsletters. I would have gotten discouraged one too many times and quit if you hadn't kept in touch with me."

"Also," they say, "I make sure to read them, because in every one you say something that no one else would dare say. Curiosity keeps me reading."

You don't have to be talented to write a good newsletter. The "rules" are simple. Keep it short. One page, back and front, or less. Make the print big enough for older folk to read. Make it interesting. Tell stories, give testimonials, mention people's names, make it as newsy and as personal as possible without being too dumb. I keep people up to date on my personal life and successes and failures. Otherwise, people start thinking that I'm a little bronzed multilevel paragon that they couldn't possibly emulate.

Keep in mind that not everyone likes or understands numbers. I've had pages of newsletters sent to me that were all numbers and marketing plan adaptations and fingalings, and circles on circles with imaginary money earned and spent in the millions. Some people love that stuff, but most of us don't. Other people just don't like to read a lot. Try and keep a nice, gentle mix.

Here are some excerpts from a few of my newsletters. Of course, I've deleted company and product information, but you will put it in to keep your people up to date.

Newsletter

Venus Hits The Skids

Dear Friends,

It seems like it's been quite awhile since we last spoke. That's because I had another crisis in my life. Every once in awhile I seem to have these huge life explosions and I drop beneath the surface of the water for a time. About six weeks ago, the man I'd been dating for five years ran off with a married friend of mine that he'd known for five days.

All I can say is, "Thank God for my multilevel business." It just pumped right along without me. Last month my check was even bigger than the month before. This is what you're working for. When you have your personal breakdowns and blow-ups, can you take to your bed for two months? Or do you have to go and file papers and grin at salespeople when you would rather be at home screaming and throwing up? I worked hard for the luxury of having the time to roll in my emotional pits. It took me about two years of night and day work around my "real" job. It may take you three or four or more years because you may not have the MLM background that I had.

Think about it. If you don't keep plugging along in your business, where will you be in five years? What else is there that can give you this kind of money and freedom? It's the best game happening, and if you're nervous about playing it, you might as well resign yourself to eating peanuts instead of fancy pecans.

A Note From Loraine

"A woman died and went to Heaven, which was more beautiful than she'd ever imagined. She couldn't wait to show it to her husband when he arrived because he was an eternal pessimist.

"A year later her husband joined her, and she took him on a tour. 'The sky, the music, the flowers,' she said, 'Heaven is truly beautiful, isn't it?'

"Her husband surveyed Paradise, then said, 'Sure, and if it weren't for you and your doggoned (healthy MLM product) we'd have been here five years sooner!'"

That's An Odd Thing To Do

I want to comment on something I've watched happen in different groups for awhile now. Sometimes upline will borrow product from their downline—not a terrific idea to begin with—then they never pay it back and act like it's no big deal! I don't understand this. Upline should be trying to *build* their downline for their own happy retirement.

I look at these people and think, "Why would you deliberately cheat your downline, make them hate you, and grin while you do it? It's like tying your leg to the underside of a moving truck on purpose."

Andrew Knocks Out Florida

Because of the hurricane, some of our group in Florida lost everything. When I called Susan and Dawn they were in shock. They and their homes were okay, but they had no electricity or water. However, most of their downlines had lost their homes and places of business. This meant that Susan and Dawn had lost their businesses, too.

It took about a month, but the girls are now up on their feet and are determinedly building their MLM businesses up again, from scratch, as are the people under them.

In this business, you'll find that many times you have to start all over again, but it's usually not because of a hurricane! This group of people aren't quitters, and it'll be a joy to see how they rebuild from almost nothing and be stronger then ever.

Please think of what they're having to do when you're feeling that all your people are gone and you have to rebuild, too.

The Montana Muse

I was talking to Virginia in Montana the other day. She's a beautiful lady who's been with me for five years. She said she'd just gone through her home office and tossed out every flyer, paper, and old dried-up product sample she had. She was ruthless. I said I'd done the same thing once before and felt so relieved afterward. I keep everything as simple as possible around here. . .and that means "cheap," too. I don't waste my money on things. My money goes for product and some necessary things like a few videos, audios, and MLM training books.

Remember The Company Conference Call March 22nd. Call 1-800-000-0000

❖❖❖Company Seminar July 15th.❖❖❖

Be sure to sign up for this before June 10th. Your group volume must equal fifty cases of product to qualify to join us in Panama City, Florida.

Please contact me if I can help you. 619-788-0000

Love, *Venus*

Assignment: Write up your own newsletter.

Mailing Lists

(See p. 179 in *MLM Magic*.)

The newsletter is the best form of advertising I have. Therefore, it's important to keep a mailing list. Collect names, addresses, and phone numbers of people who are interested in what you have to offer, or people you think will be, as well as your present downline. At first, you will probably be able to hand-address your newsletters, but as your list grows, you will need to do something else. Go to the copy shop and get some Avery or Dennison labels. There is usually a frame you can put behind a sheet of paper that will show you where to type in the names. Type them on a sheet of plain paper, then put the labels in the copy machine and copy your list onto the labels. This works great until your list gets longer and the changes are more frequent.

If your mailing list fills up your Rolodex and gets so bulky you begin to wonder if it's worth it, it's time to think about getting a computer. If you've been typing your list and running it off on the copier, you will definitely find a computer an improvement.

I'll have to admit that I find computers intimidating. Fortunately, I have a mother and daughter who love them. You don't need a super-hyped up computer filled with megabytes and RAM and whatever else they put on them. I have a simple, basic computer, a word processing program for writing my newsletter, and a database program for storing names and addresses. I'd also recommend a hard drive for storing all this data, although most computers sold nowadays have one built-in. Years ago, my mother had her whole accounting system on one floppy disk instead of a hard drive. The computer gave her a "disk full" signal: she panicked and hit the return key. Her whole accounting system never returned.

I have a Macintosh SE with one megabyte of RAM and a twenty meg hard drive. The Macintosh is easy to learn, compared to what else is out there. I'd recommend shopping the classifieds if you have a computer literate friend willing to help you. Otherwise, find a store where the clerks are patient and willing to help you find what's best for you, and who welcome phone calls after you've brought a computer home. Prices have come down a lot since I bought my computer for over $2,000. Be sure to get a printer that works with your computer. My sister Candy has an SE without a hard drive. Her husband wanted to get her a printer for Christmas. Most printers require a computer to have two megs of RAM and a hard drive to operate. So he gave her the money to buy her own hard drive and printer because he was so baffled, and she spent it on Christmas presents for the rest of the family.

I use my computer to whip out my newsletters, keep my mailing list current, and print out labels.

. . .A note about these last few paragraphs: As Mom was reading the first draft of this workbook, she decided that I needed to mention something about computers. Since I don't know anything about them, she decided it would be best if she wrote this section. So, masquerading as me, she did. I certainly hope you enjoyed it. I thought it was pretty interesting. But I have a few things to add, in my own words: I'm able to use a computer to type my books, newsletters, and mailing lists too. That's the only relationship I have with a computer. It goes no deeper.

Once I tuck my newsletters into envelopes and stick on the labels, I always add a handwritten note on the outside. I like to do it and I think people like to get a personal message from me, too. Being personal in this business is important.

9

Business Tips

Taxes

(See pp. 192-195 in *MLM Magic*.)

When I first started in multilevel, I went to an MLM seminar where the featured speaker was a tax consultant. He spent two hours raving that if we weren't in multilevel yet, get in fast, because the business is loaded with tax write-offs. Among the things he spoke about were home office deductions, including partial write-offs for electricity, phone, part of the house, gardening, a housekeeper, and parties. You have to give parties and take people to lunch, for heaven's sake. Even driving to your real job and stopping at your postal box to pick up all your MLM leads is a write off. You can spend a few hours during your "vacation" signing up your Aunt Tissie in Oregon and Uncle Filbert in Hawaii. There are tax write-offs on that kind of travel.

After many years in this business, I tell you truly, find a good tax person. Don't get a bean counter. You want someone who will help you find every little thing you can write-off. I think I paid way too much tax for way too long before I got the help I needed. I was shedding tax people like extra skin until I found the right one for me.

I know, taxes are boring and silly and unfair, but you will find that knowing your rights will mean you either keep or give away a great deal of money.

Your assignment is to: a) do some reading about taxes related to a home business, b) talk to people who've been in multilevel for awhile and who can suggest a good tax person and who'll also tell you what they write off, c) interview recommended tax people, and d) write out everything you can think of that you may be able to deduct.

Possible Tax Deductions For My MLM Business:

_____

_____

_____

_____

_____

_____

_____

_____

_____

_____

_____

Ideas To Perk You Up When Building An MLM Business Seems Hopeless

(See pp. 243-258 in *MLM Magic*.)

Expect to have sudden dips into depression and despair when you're building a multilevel business, even long after you've put your business together. After seven years in mine, I still get them. I know this doesn't sound cheery, but it's realistic. MLM is utterly both the best business in the world and the worst. I think there are more crises and disappointments in multilevel than in any other career. There are, however, many more ecstatic moments and chances to make huge amounts of money than in most other careers. You don't get opportunities like these by driving a bus or working in an office. If you've decided to jump into multilevel with the rest of us, you must toughen up.

Here's another typical slice out of my life. Remember, I've

been doing this for a long time and I'm successful. I make more money than most people in this country, yet, as I keep my business going, I still face what you deal with, too. I just may be more used to it.

This morning, as I settle down at my kitchen table to answer some mail and send off a few product samples, the phone rings. It's Denny. I've never met Denny, but he calls me every day, often two or three times a day. He read one of my books about a month ago, contacted me, and eventually signed into the business. He's been so excited he can't sleep. Every day he's been on the phone with me planning his new business. He's even planned to order a significant amount of product so he can reach a top level right away. I'm thinking, "Thank you, God, I've been needing someone like Denny. It's been a long time since I signed someone who's really done something."

Tonight, in fact, I'll be at a meeting I've set up as a special home meeting near Denny so I can meet him and do some in-person training. Denny's now on the phone, and I'm saying, "I can hardly wait to meet you tonight, Denny!"

Denny says, "Ah, that's why I'm calling."

I think, "Oh no. This meeting is basically for him! What's his excuse? And why? He's been so excited about all of this." But I say, "What do you mean?"

"Well, I can't make it tonight," he says. Then he tells me that not only can he not make it, but he has an appointment to see a woman to sell her something from another multilevel that he's working in. He says he has to do it because he needs the money. In fact, he's sure that he can make more money with this other multilevel than in mine, and while he sure wants to keep his hand in with my MLM, he won't be able to buy *any* product.

I'm dumb-founded, but I say, "I'm expecting to see you at that meeting tonight, Denny. Things are going to work out so you'll be there."

Denny breathes a weak, "Heh heh."

I think, "Boy. Isn't this the way multilevel often is. Why do I keep doing it?" I'm thinking this as I'm writing a note and wrapping up product samples to send off to yet another person who will never do anything with the business.

As I'm muttering and moaning to myself I'm thinking about another lady I called yesterday and haven't heard from. About three weeks ago, I met Irene at a class. We spent time discussing her life and mine and marvel of marvels she insisted on joining me in my MLM.

Several days later, I'd driven an hour to see her and spent three hours signing her up and talking to her. She proudly told me that she'd already ordered her business cards and had a great idea for the weekend. She was going to sell our products at a Home Fair where she'd be working, so she wanted a lot of product on hand.

"Wait a minute," I said. "You've never been in multilevel before. You don't want to buy a huge amount of stuff and expect to sell it all this weekend. I've worked fairs, and they work well for some people, but not for me. People don't just race up to you and yell, "Sell me six bottles of that stuff! I don't know what it is, but I like your looks and you must have a great something here. Sure bet I need it."

Irene just looked at me. "It'll be easy," she finally said. I knew she was beginning to wonder how I did so well in multilevel if I couldn't even sell stuff at a fair.

"It's not like you think," I persisted. I was wrestling with myself a bit. I hated to discourage a shiny new distributor, but I couldn't let her walk merrily into a huge disappointment. That would be even worse. "There are lots of things to buy at home shows. Lots of booths. Lots of competition and diversions. You're going to have to talk to lots of people, and most will drink and eat and rub your samples all over their body and through their hair and that'll be the end of it. They'll toss your brochures in the trash as they turn the corner. You may get lucky and sell a few things, and you might get even luckier and sign someone up, but you might not. You're new at this and you've never sold anything. You'll learn as you go, I'll teach you all I know, but don't expect too much this weekend."

"Oh don't worry," Irene said. "I know I'll be good at this."

On Monday I called Irene. Things hadn't gone well.

"Have you sent in my distributor application?" she asked.

"No," I said, "I was waiting to see how many cases you wanted to order. You were toying with six last weekend and I want to make sure you can monetarily handle that."

"Don't turn it in," she said. "I have to do my taxes. I'll call you in three days."

I haven't heard from Irene since, and she's also supposed

to be at that meeting tonight.

One thing that causes me grief with people like Denny and Irene is that they're often totally without multilevel experience. When they step off the pier and into our waters, they often go straight down, never to be seen again. Also, many of the people attracted to multilevel (not including us, of course), are strange. They're just odd in some way. Sometimes they're the people who've never been able to be successful before. Or, they don't have common business sense, so they do things like Denny did, suddenly signing into another multilevel because that group convinced him he could make big money instantly. It helps to remember this when you have disappointments like mine. It's not necessarily or even likely your fault. You've just been working with a certain kind of person that isn't quite right for multilevel. The old answer to that, of course, is "*next.*" Just look for someone else, and someone else, and someone else until you find a few good people.

But, back to my day. Some days are like this. There is more to come.

Two letters. One is from my downline, Patricia, telling me why her business has faltered. According to her, the company has ruined one of her downline and cost her $880 a month. On top of that, one of her upline is jealous of her and has had a hand in her business and money losses. She also says that she didn't make it to the last big company meeting because her royalty checks are so low she couldn't afford to go. She ended by saying, "But, then you are aware of these things." I wasn't.

The other letter is from Scotty. He said he'd had a chat with one of our upline who told him that none of us are in this business to help people, that we're all just in it for money, and that's all anyone is interested in, and to forget any other ideas. Just talk money to people, and get out there and build the business. Scotty says he took exception to this and reminded me that I've always taught him to keep a balance and to try to help people with our products. He says everyone else in our group feels the same way—that money and the business are very important, but that loving and believing in our products is *more* important, so what's this new tack about "forget all that and just make a buck?"

Well folks, you can't control your upline. Or your downline. In fact, you can't control anybody. Another way to lessen the grief of multilevel is to realize that you can't control what anyone thinks or does. You do your best, and eventually, the best will come to you. Eventually.

Drainers can also cause you grief. These are people in your downline who are chronically negative. For example, there's a Drainer in my group

85

who calls me at least once or twice a week with all the current company and personal scandals. She decided long ago that she has no respect for the company, the company CEO, and most of the rest of us. Still, she cries anyway and demands to know why people aren't little gold-coated gods like she expects them to be. For much too long I listened and advised and tried to explain human nature, but I've since stopped. What brought my patience to an end was a conversation with her that made me feel so ill I took a nap for three hours. (And that cuts into the business day.)

Another of my downline, Kate, has a running feud with her so-called "best" downline, a woman named Maria. Kate calls me all the time and tells me about the screaming differences of opinion they have, about the name calling, and the distrust. I say, "Kate, quick, sign somebody else up."

"I have," Kate wails, "but Maria is my best downline. And she's so negative and she accuses me of lying to her and she says she can't trust me and I'm in pain all the time with her attitude."

"Kate," I say, after hearing all this for months, "it sounds like a bad relationship. If she were your boyfriend, I hope you'd have the sense to get rid of her. Do the same now. Cut off contact. You're making yourself nuts."

Kate can't do it, so she keeps on suffering.

My advice? If you have people who cause you this kind of emotional upset, either lessen or stop the contact. Also, a great antidote for these kinds of people is to call someone else in your downline (or anyone you know) who has a great attitude about life and likes to laugh. I usually call Peter. You remember Peter from *MLM Magic*. He's the one who slips his company magazine to strangers under bathroom stalls in big hotels. After six years, Peter is still just as excited about his business as he was the day he started. In fact, I've made a rule that he can't call me after 9:30 at night because he gets me so wound up about all the money he's going to make me that I can't go to sleep.

I'm not through with my day, yet. I get a phone call canceling a class I was to teach tomorrow that was actually going to make me money. I get another call canceling lunch with a business prospect and, of course, I have that in-home meeting tonight. Since the day is rolling a certain way, I won't be too surprised if after I drive an hour to get there, no one but the hosts and I will show up.

What do you do with days like these? As soon as I notice there's a run of these kinds of things, I stop what I'm doing and do something totally different. In this case, I'm writing. But, I might just put the phone on answer and go uptown to the coffee shop. Or I might read a book. Or go fiddle in the garden. It's almost like breaking a spell, and it works. Generally, when I get back to business, everything is okay, again.

As for day to day disappointments? You just have to realize that when the opportunity for big profits exists, opportunities for big disappointments also exist.

Being a writer, I hear all the stories about people who write books for years and years and never get published, or who send manuscripts out hundreds of times before a publisher buys one. Then, overnight, it seems, they become famous millionaires.

I can tell you a funny story about me. I wrote a book called *The Herb Lady's Notebook.* Just by word of mouth, it's sold about 50,000 copies (which is unusual). A few years ago, I got a call from a famous agent who had seen that book and wanted to see if she could sell it to a big publishing house. (Famous agents generally don't go looking for you. I felt like I'd been struck by heavenly lightening.) Sure enough, she got the book to an editor in a big publishing house who loved it. In fact, the editor was crazy about it. The publishing house planned to buy my book and put me on tour all over the country. That meant radio and television talk shows. The editor was going to make me a star. I was giddy, and grinning, and pretty darn happy.

Then, silence. Nothing. Finally, my agent called. She was very embarrassed. The deal was off. As so often happens in publishing, the editor who had loved my book had been removed and replaced with another. The new editor hated, loathed, and despised my book. All deals were off.

My agent expected me to collapse and die. I didn't. I started laughing. Fame is short, and fame is fleet, but I hadn't realized mine would be *that* short. It struck me as enormously funny, perhaps because I didn't take it personally. I knew I had more life to live and that other interesting things would happen. My book was still alive and out there and I'd write more books because I loved to write—and who knows what might still transpire?

It's the same with multilevel. A lot of work seems wasted. But, it's not.

Dealing with Discouragement

Everything you do—every failed meeting, dissatisfied retail customer, or difficult distributor is *practice* as you make your way to a decent or even extraordinary living. You're waiting and working and expecting the best. . .and not taking disappointments personally.

Your next assignment is to create a list of ways to combat discouragement. Here is my list:

<u>What I'm Going To Do And Remember When I'm Depressed And Discouraged With MLM:</u>

1. I will remember I'm working this business to get the money to buy my own house.
2. I will remember that it only takes *one good person* to build my retirement.
3. I will remember to stop and do something entirely different if a negative pattern is emerging for the day.
4. I know that everybody goes through this.
5. I know that if I quit now, I'll never have that brass harmonica, that new car, a life of my own, etc.
6. I will ask myself, "Who or what is causing me this pain and do I really need to deal with it?"
7. I will remember that even if only one person shows at my meeting, they might become my star distributor—or, they might sign someone who will outperform both of us.
8. I will call everyone I know who has a good attitude.
9. I accept that I can't control people.
10. I can always go uptown and sit in a coffee shop and eat sunflower seeds.

What I'm Going To Do And Remember When I'm Depressed And Discouraged With MLM:

_____

_____

_____

_____

_____

_____

_____

_____

_____

_____

_____

_____

_____

_____

_____

_____

_____

_____

_____

_____

_____

_____

_____

_____

10

Direct Your Thoughts

In closing, I'd like to remind you of something important that's become popular lately, and even overdone and a bit tiresome. It's this: While building your business (and living your life) *direct your thoughts*. Don't just watch your thoughts as most people advise, but formulate and direct them, because what you think is what you get, and what you think is what you become.

If you're how I used to be, you may not even be aware that your mind, which is supposed to be obedient to you and primed to do your will, has actually taken control of your life, your health, your relationships, your future, your everything. In reality, this so-called servant of yours is telling you what you think, what you feel, and how you'll live. Stop a minute and watch it, and you'll see what I mean.

Pause a moment now, sit back, take about five or ten minutes, and think about building your business.

After having done that, reflect on how many other thoughts intruded. Did you find your mind wondering if you fed your dogs or if you're smart enough to make money in multilevel? Were you thinking about the sex life you wish you had, or did you find yourself watching your neighbor water his lawn while you noticed and judged the way his jeans rode down on his white behind? Were you feeling hungry, or wishing you hadn't eaten so much today, and wondering how much fatter you might get, etc.?

Most minds are a mess, rife with conflicting thoughts and a morass of brackish and beautiful emotions.

In order to get where you want to be with your business, you must get a rein on your mind. It may help you to know where some of this mind

91

garbage comes from. Last night, I watched an interview on TV with an autistic woman. An autistic person is someone who is locked inside himself and supposedly unreachable, with no emotions or human feelings. Autistic people often lash out at themselves and exhibit what regular people think of as bizarre actions. They don't converse with people, and they certainly don't write books or have relationships. Yet, this woman has written two best-selling books, has a boyfriend, and a real life.

What struck me is this: She explained that as an autistic person, she was completely out of touch with herself. She copied the actions of everyone and everything around her. She mimicked gestures, speaking voices, habits—everything. She said she spent years finding herself. She says she knows that she makes odd gestures, walks strangely, and speaks in a wavering voice. "But," she said, "it's my voice. It's not your voice. See," she continued, as she slipped into an English accent, "I can perfectly copy any accent, any hand movement, any style of anyone else." She paused a moment as she began to cry. "It's so hard to be myself. I have to think about and remember who I am, at every moment, or I think and act out everyone else's selves and ideas."

The day after hearing this interview, I was reviewing it in my mind. Suddenly, I felt like I'd been thwacked by a frying pan. "My gosh," I thought, "that woman is out mimicking what all of us are like, except she knows it," while we seemingly normal people live our lives in a trance. Unknowingly, unwittingly, we think and feel and do and say what our minds have been taught and trained to do since we were born! It's time to wake up, as this woman did.

Who are you, really? What do you want to be like? How do you want to live your life? Do you really believe you can't succeed at multilevel, or is that your mother's thoughts? Do you think you have to have a nine to five job and retire on pension, or is that your father's and his father's and his father's idea?

I was talking to a friend the other day. At forty-two, after nineteen years of marriage, she's just gotten a divorce. She said, "I'm finding out who I am now. I'm writing lists of things I had forgotten I liked, like pansies and yellow walls and Saab cars. My husband never liked those things, so I thought I didn't. He hates the color green. Now, I'm buying everything green!"

Diane proudly pointed to her green sweat shirt and pants.

"It's a good thing you look good in green," I said.

"And," she whispered, "I despise my business. Yesterday I was typing up escrow papers and I thought, 'I hate doing this.'" She looked at me and said, "I didn't know I hated my business until I started thinking for myself—until I took a good look at those thoughts in my head. My husband always liked my doing real estate because it paid all the bills! I wonder what else is going to show up in my head that isn't mine?"

To find out more about what's in your mind (you can wonder if they're even your thoughts, later, and take steps to change them), it helps to start by sitting quietly and listening to your breath. Breathe in, breathe out. Breathe in, breathe out. Don't control the breathing, let it stop and start however it wants. Now, do you see those thoughts skittering through your mind like scruffy coated cockroaches while you breathe? Ignore them. Let them skitter. Kind of stand back and watch all those thoughts, but don't jump in with them.

After you've done this for awhile—and *awhile* means at various times, on scattered days—try something different. While you're relaxed, breathing, and paying no attention to the jumble and jangle of thoughts that have hung themselves off your mind's branches like Christmas lights, do something deliberate: *Choose what you want to think and think it.* With practice, you can really make changes in your life. You'll also change your character, and probably even your appearance for the better. Practice, practice, practice.

Also practice having positive thoughts every waking moment. This does not mean becoming a Happy Jolly Pollyanna in the face of disappointments, frustrations, and tragedies. That kind of forced thinking puts stress on a person.

For example, I had a husband once who took advantage of me all the time, sat around all day in his undershorts watching TV, and eventually took my money, my house, and my business. He even managed to put his foot in my reputation and rub it around and influence many of my friends. After the divorce, people looked at little pin-headed me and said, "Poor Venus. Poor, poor Venus."

Within several years, nobody said that anymore. After the divorce, as I sat in the dark emotional pit I'd dug, I said to myself, "Obviously, I made some bad choices with that man and that marriage. What did I do, why did I do it, and how can I prevent it from ever happening again?" I put a good face on the experience. *I changed the way I'd learned to think.* My old way of thinking had brought me the Bad Husband Experience. Today, that man still has the same miserable life he had many years ago—and you know how I'm doing!

Remember what grownups used to tell you when you were little? "If you keep thinking those ugly thoughts and making those ugly faces, your face will freeze that way." I used to think they were trying to scare the meanness out of me. (Remember the tea party?) But, now I know they were telling the truth.

The other day I saw a woman in her fifties who used to be beautiful. I was struck by how ugly she'd become. It wasn't age that did it. Thelma always had a little trouble with resentment and envy of other people. She even went out of her way to wish them ill health and misfortune. I don't know about her victims, but poor Thelma now looks like old, chewed dogmeat. Her acid thoughts have melted her face.

The sight of Thelma's face made a little saint outa' me! I make it a practice to wish everybody and everything (including myself, and even Thelma) the best the Universe has to offer.

Ugly or negative thoughts will show on your face, and they will also show in the circumstances that surround you in your life.

If you don't like the way you're living, know that your previous thoughts, beliefs, and conditioning brought you to where you are now. The word *conditioning* is important. Maybe most of your thoughts aren't what *you* really believe at all! Don't let them determine your life. Seek them out and get rid of them. This will change your future.

Your last assignment is to start writing all the beliefs you have about yourself, your life, the gov-

ernment, your business, money, and your world that may be blocking your progress. Don't expect to get them all on this page. I suspect this is a lifetime occupation.

_____

_____

_____

_____

_____

_____

_____

_____

_____

_____

_____

Good wishes, good luck, much success, and I'm throwing good will, money, and happiness all over you!

Love, *Venus*

To contact Venus, please send a **self-addressed, stamped** *envelope* to:
Venus Andrecht
PO Box 2435
Ramona, Ca 92065

Ransom Hill Press Books
A Family Publishing Company

MLM Magic, V. Andrecht.   16.95_____
Award winning book teaching how to become successful in multilevel.
MLM Magic (Spanish version), V. Andrecht.   18.95_____
MLM Magic Workbook, V. Andrecht.   18.95_____
Companion to MLM Magic, the Workbook includes more new material on developing your multilevel and is designed for you to write in as it guides you in a strategy for success.
The Herb Lady's Notebook, V. Andrecht.   16.95_____
A funny and informational account of the nutritional uses of herbs. Venus describes true case histories from her years as an herbalist.
The Outrageous Herb Lady, V. Andrecht.   12.95_____
A mix of multilevel and herbal information, written in Venus' usual easy and lighthearted style.
"Dear Venus"   5.95_____
A collection of "Dear Venus" columns previously published in magazines, newspapers, and multilevel trade journals.

Audio Cassette Series:

Tape #1—Money Out of Control Audio Cassette and Booklet, V. Andrecht.   9.95_____
Venus describes how to control your finances in MLM.
Tape #2—Prospecting Audio Cassette and Booklet, V. Andrecht. Coming Fall of '94, call for price.   _____
Venus gives more valuable tips on how and where to find distributors, as well as how to train them.

Other Ransom Hill Press Titles:

Tea Cup Tales, M. McWhorter.   5.95_____
An insightful and easy guide to reading tea leaves.
Poems That Tell Me Who I Am, M. McWhorter.   4.95_____
A volume of uplifting poetry by Venus' own mother.
Autumn Leaves, M. McWhorter.   4.95_____
A second book of beautiful verses by Mrs. McWhorter.
Drift On The River, P. Rozelle.   9.95_____
A work of fiction by Venus' aunt about a stay in Alabama in the theme of Thoreau's *Walden*.

Payment Enclosed/Charge my: Mastercard___ Visa___

Card #:_____Exp. date:_____

Name:_____Phone:_____

Address:_____

City:_____State:_____Zip:_____

Tax (CA):_____

Shipping:_____

Total:_____

California residents add appropriate sales tax.
Shipping: $2.00 for first book, $.50 each additional book. Priority mail, $3.50 first book, $.50 2nd book. For COD, UPS, Priority, and shipping out of the country, please call for rates.

For Visa or Mastercard orders call: 1-800-423-0620
U.S. & Canada. Out of U.S. dial (619) 789-0620

Make checks payable to:
Ransom Hill Press
PO Box 325 Ramona, CA 92065-0325   **Call for Volume Discounts!**
Fax: (619) 789-1582   Prices subject to change without notice.